"Yoga is the best thing I've done for myself, mentally, physically, and spiritually. Ally's heart for people and love for Jesus is incredibly inspiring and has taken me to a whole new level. You're not going to want to miss out on what she has to share for you!"

—Stevi Hillman
8x Wrangler National Finals Rodeo Qualifier

"I highly recommend this invaluable book for Christians wanting Godly wisdom when trekking the world of yoga. Expect this truth-filled guide to stretch your faith positively and become a credible resource when addressing concerns about faith and yoga."

—Miranda Davis
Author of *Christian Girl in the Yoga World: Biblical Wisdom to Safely Navigate the Practice and Honor Your Faith*

Physical & Spiritual STRETCHING

Ally McCrory

LUCIDBOOKS

Physical and Spiritual Stretching

Published by Lucid Books in Houston, TX

www.LucidBooks.com

ISBN: 978-1-63296-660-5

eISBN: 978-1-63296-661-2

Special Sales: Most Lucid Books titles are available in special quantity discounts. Custom imprinting or excerpting can also be done to fit special needs. Contact Lucid Books at Info@LucidBooks.com

FOREWORD
MARC OWENS
Founder, elevateHim Ministries

My name is Marc Owings and I am the founder of elevateHim Ministries. I meet thousands of people each year but what an honor to know Ally and her husband Cody!

I met Ally for the first time at a Fully Alive women's event in Weatherford, Texas in 2012. I could sense when she came into the room that she needed kindness and a safe place. As the weekend unfolded at Fully Alive I watched Jesus become her hero! I could see Jesus was lovingly washing away bitterness, anger, shame, and disappointment. It was such a privilege to watch Ally choose forgiveness and freedom that weekend.

Since that weekend many years ago I have watched not only Ally but her husband Cody truly live a life for Jesus Christ. If you have the privilege to meet with her or her husband you will discover that the main focus for her and them is simply Jesus Christ! She will be the first to share that Jesus is her protector, comforter and best friend.

I am so honored to witness the Holy Spirit establishing her in an industry that has been stereotyped as new age yoga mantras at best and at worst a total disregard for King Jesus. So many believers become fearful about this industry and the incredible benefits we all can experience through physical and spiritual stretching. The yoga industry better get ready for a woman who knows she is, a Daughter of the King! As a friend and a brother I simply want to sit and watch Jesus shine through Ally as she brings health, healing and love to people.

—Marc Owens
Founder, elevateHim Ministries

TABLE OF CONTENTS

INTRODUCTION
YOGA FOR YAHWEH

I have been a Christian my whole life, and I have practiced yoga for several years. There were times when I wasn't an active Christian and going to church on Sundays. There were also times when I was absent from my practice in yoga. In either case, it didn't make me less of a Christian or someone who loved the yoga world.

I found yoga, or better put, the Lord led me to yoga shortly after my daughter was born. I needed a release, and I wasn't attending church at that time. I went to the gym and took group fitness classes, but it didn't really stick, and eventually I stopped going.

Fast-forward a few years. My marriage hit a brick wall . . . hard; I found myself needing a physical release, and I found hot yoga in a dance studio where I worked.

We were going to church, but only going through the motions. My heart and mind continued to sing the song "Nothing Else" by Cody Carnes, which has the following lyrics: "I'm sorry . . . I'm just going through the motions. I'm sorry I just sang another song." I went to church, but I didn't really go to church. I was more like a zombie that was barely making it on coffee, cigarettes, and more caffeine.

I continued to practice yoga and really fell in love with the brain and body connection. I had numbed myself out for a while, and it was refreshing to feel again. I attended a teacher training session to obtain a 200-hour registered yoga teacher certification and dove into a whole new world of ideologies and theories.

My marriage finally disintegrated in 2015, and I went to Boston to pursue more yoga training. Then I went to New York to do group training with Baron Baptiste for his level-one program. At this point I had made it through a 200-hour teacher training, a weekend of the Art of Assisting, and the Level One program. I was ready to begin my teaching journey.

I found a small space that could hold six mats. Three months after I got the keys to the small space, the Lord opened another door to a much bigger space next door. It surpasses my understanding how I thrived during that time. The only explanation is that the Lord had me, and He wasn't about to let me go. Owning a small business is hard work with no breaks and long hours and no time to be a mother to my daughter. It was just me running the studio for a few months, and then I started to bring on some instructors to help with the class loads. I was a single mom running a business, holding down a house that needed repairs, and making sure my daughter was taken care of. It was difficult, but the Lord was faithful and blessed me with an ex-husband who took outstanding care of his daughter.

As things continued to grow at the studio, so did my faith. I began attending a sweet little church and felt right at home. Things on the dating front were also looking up and positive! I was blessed to meet my new husband, Cody, at the yoga studio one evening while he was taking a class. So, we began to attend the same church, and we are still members and leaders in that church.

When you grow in your faith, so does your knowledge of the Word and discernment for things that don't line up with His Word. Several Christian church members questioned me about doing yoga and questioned my faith in the Lord because yoga is seen as a tribute to the gods in the Eastern culture. Yoga became something I wasn't entirely sure I still wanted to be a part of and that was detrimental to my career and lifestyle.

I decided to do extensive research on my own and listen to hear what the Lord had to say about yoga and Christians. Where did yoga originate? And why was it supposedly contradictory to Christianity and belief in Jesus? I discovered that yoga originated in India around AD 1500; the issue here is that yoga is based on Hindu/Buddhist belief systems. These religions have several gods and deities unlike Christianity in which we believe in one God with three facets: Father, Son, and Holy Spirit.

> *You shall not make idols for yourselves or erect an image or a sacred pillar, and you shall not set up a figured stone in your land to bow down to it; for I am the Lord your God.*
> —Leviticus 26:1 ESV

> *This wicked people, who refuse to listen to My words, who walk in the stubbornness of their hearts and have gone after other gods to serve them and to bow down to them, let them be just like this waistband which is totally worthless.*
> — Jeremiah 13:10 NASB 1995

But in all reality, who really created it all? The stars and the moon, the heavens and the seas? It was all created by God; He is the master creator and force behind all things.

All things were made by Him; and without Him was not anything made that was made.

—John 1:3 KJV

For in him all things were created; things in heaven and on earth, visible and invisible, whether thrones or powers or rulers or authorities; all things have been created through him and for him.

—Colossians 1:16

This is where the dilemma comes in: If God created all things, then why would yoga be considered dangerous to Christians? He created our body, and yoga is a tool He created for us to help take care of the temple He has given us.

Or do you not know that your body is a temple of the Holy Spirit within you, whom you have from God? You are not your own, for you were bought with a price. So, glorify God in your body.

—1 Corinthians 6:19–20 ESV

The more research I did, the more apparent it became to me that God was the one who created yoga in the first place. But the enemy has twisted what God made and tried to keep Christians from using it because of a lack of understanding and fear. The enemy does not want believers to have something that can be beneficial to their bodies in a way of self-healing and without prescriptions.

You intended to harm me, but God intended it for good to accomplish what is now being done, the saving of many lives.

—Genesis 50:20

This book is my love song and praise to a great God who has given us the capability to help heal and find peace to sit with him on our mat. Yoga and Christianity *can* coexist. Where the spirit of the Lord is, there is peace. That is my biggest prayer for you. I pray you have ease of the heart and no judgment from others about doing an exercise for your body and mind.

Following each chapter there will be a Reflection Section that I have shared in my classes during times of self-inquiry and reflection. This section can be a simple small story or a deeper more thoughtout process, but the Reflection Section should be a time that allows you to continue to reflect and connect. The next section "Let's Get Froggy" is a good example.

Let's Get Froggy

I must share a story that I recently shared with my yoga classes.

I was eating my lunch when I saw a huge toad in my pool, so I ran out there in the rain to pull him out. When I got there, I realized that it wasn't just one toad but two and the little guy on top was squeezing the big one almost to death! He was relying on the big one to carry him around and save him.

So, I plucked them out of the pool and took them over to the fence. The little one's arms were wrapped so tightly around the big one that I had to pry them apart! I finally got them apart and went inside to finish lunch.

I am always looking for a lesson in all the events that I see. So, I was looking for what God wanted to teach me about this one. I googled what it meant when two frogs were stuck together like that.

Welp, they were mating, and I ruined it! But I saved their little lives from drowning.

So, the lesson from the Lord? Laugh. Laugh until your cheeks hurt and your head hurts. He basically showed me that I needed to

5

relax and stop always looking for lessons being taught. Just enjoy what is happening and laugh when you can.

So, I shook my head when I found out what was happening, laughed, and apologized to the toads for breaking up their good time . . .

STAND FIRM AND BE OBEDIENT

> *For if you remain silent at this time, relief and deliverance for the Jews will arise from another place, but you and your father's family will perish. And who knows but that you have come to your royal position for such a time as this?*
>
> —Esther 4:14

Perhaps you were born for such a time as this. As a yoga community, we usually ended our classes by saying Namaste, which expresses the idea that "the light in me honors the light in you, and we are at the highest place in our lives; we are one." This was the standard ending to each class, and I never thought much about it. That is, until I felt like the Lord was asking me to change it. The word He wanted me to begin using was *Agape*, which is a Greek word that means unconditional love—a love in which we put others' needs above our own. Just like God's love.

In the beginning of 2021, I decided to change the ending of my classes from Namaste to Agape. It was a change that took lots of prayer and discernment, and even after all that, I still didn't want to do it even though I was clearly feeling the Lord tugging a my heart to do so.

God had given me the studio, and now He wanted me to change it in a drastic way. I was hesitant, but I went with it knowing that in my obedience, He would shine.

Doubt, criticism, and negative feedback began to accumulate in my mind: "*Who do you think you are? You are not qualified or educated enough to make changes to the yoga community. You are not important enough to make such big changes and change the way the yoga community is led.*"

These thoughts did not stem from Jesus, so they obviously came from the enemy. Maybe he was right because some students and instructors did not feel comfortable with the change, and they left the studio. It knocked me down for a short time, but then God reminded me who I am, and with a little help from a sweet friend, Miranda Jo Davis, I began to turn the situation around. I was reminded that the people who left were only making way for other people to come—my people—the people who need what I offer. Those who left had created the space necessary for growth to begin.

So, who am I? I came to understand that holding space here in this yoga studio and creating a place for people to feel His love is His mission for me, and no one else has to understand besides God and me; it was communicated in a private meeting between the two of us. Remember that no one needs to understand your calling from God; it was not a conference call. He tells us to not conform to the world (Romans 12:2).

Don't let others dumb down your faith. If your faith intimidates others, that may be a sign that they are learning from you in the process. Sometimes, the hard things need to be said in order to grow. If you know God is leading you, put down your insecurities and be obedient. He wants you to prosper in all ways.

> *If you fully obey the LORD your God and carefully follow all his commands I give you today, the LORD your God will set you high above all the nations on earth. All these blessings will come on you and*

accompany you if you obey the LORD your God: You
will be blessed in the city and blessed in the country.
The fruit of your womb will be blessed, and the crops
of your land and the young of your livestock—the
calves of your herds and the lambs of your flocks. Your
basket and your kneading trough will be blessed. You
will be blessed when you come in and blessed when
you go out.

—Deuteronomy 28:1–6

Noah didn't stop building the ark to explain himself to every doubter and critic. Keep building, and let the rain do the talking. God doesn't call the qualified; he qualifies the called. Go and do what he has called you to do—today.

CHAPTER ONE
WHO CREATED IT ALL?

In the beginning God created the heavens and earth.
—Genesis 1:1

The Beginning

In the beginning God created the heavens and the earth. Now the earth was formless and empty, darkness was over the surface of the deep, and the Spirit of God was hovering over the waters.

And God said, "Let there be light," and there was light. God saw that the light was good, and he separated the light from the darkness. God called the light "day," and the darkness he called "night." And there was evening, and there was morning—the first day.

And God said, "Let there be a vault between the waters to separate water from water." So God made the vault and separated the water under the vault from the water above it. And it was so. God called the vault "sky." And there was evening, and there was morning—the second day.

And God said, "Let the water under the sky be gathered to one place, and let dry ground appear." And it was so. God called the dry ground "land," and the gathered waters he called "seas." And God saw that it was good. Then God said, "Let the land produce vegetation: seed-bearing plants and trees on the land that bear fruit with seed in it, according to their various kinds." And it was so. The land produced vegetation: plants bearing seed according to their kinds and trees bearing fruit with seed in it according to their kinds. And God saw that it was good. And there was evening, and there was morning—the third day.

And God said, "Let there be lights in the vault of the sky to separate the day from the night and let them serve as signs to mark sacred times, and days and years, and let them be lights in the vault of the sky to give light on the earth." And it was so. God made two great lights— the greater light to govern the day and the lesser light to govern the night. He also made the stars. God set them in the vault of the sky to give light on the earth, to govern the day and the night, and to separate light from darkness. And God saw that it was good. And there was evening, and there was morning—the fourth day.

And God said, "Let the water teem with living creatures, and let birds fly above the earth across the vault of the sky." So God created the great creatures of the sea and every living thing with which the water teems and that moves about in it, according to their kinds, and every winged bird according to its kind. And God saw that it was good. God blessed them and said, "Be fruitful and increase in number and fill the water in the seas, and let the birds increase on the earth." And there was evening, and there was morning—the fifth day. And God said, "Let the land produce living creatures according to their kinds: the livestock, the creatures that move along the ground, and the wild animals, each according to its kind." And it was so. God made the wild animals according to their kinds, the livestock according to their kinds, and all the creatures that move along the ground according to their kinds. And God saw that it was good.

Then God said, "Let us make mankind in our image, in our likeness, so that they may rule over the fish in the sea and the birds in the sky, over the livestock and all the wild animals, and over all the creatures that move along the ground."

So God created mankind in his own image,
in the image of God, he created them;
male and female he created them.

God blessed them and said to them, "Be fruitful and increase in number; fill the earth and subdue it. Rule over the fish in the sea and the birds in the sky and over every living creature that moves on the ground."

Then God said, "I give you every seed-bearing plant on the face of the whole earth and every tree that has fruit with seed in it. They will be yours for food. And to all the beasts of the earth and all the birds in the sky and all the creatures that move along the ground—everything that has the breath of life in it—I give every green plant for food." And it was so.

God saw all that he had made, and it was very good. And there was evening, and there was morning—the sixth day.

Thus the heavens and the earth were completed in all their vast array.

> *By the seventh day God had finished the work he had been doing; so, on the seventh day he rested from all his work. Then God blessed the seventh day and made it holy, because on it he rested from all the work of creating that he had done.*
>
> —Genesis 1:1–2:4

If God created the heavens and the earth, then he created all things—whether it may be humans, stingrays, ideas, methodologies, or stink bugs. We know that in two separate books of the Bible (Exodus 20:2–17 and Deuteronomy 5:6–21), there is a set of commandments written down by Moses. These Ten Commandments declare the way God wants us to treat our bodies and others. In Hindu, where the practice of yoga was created, there is a set of commandments called the yamas and niyamas. The yamas are a set of external values while the niyamas are a set of internal ethics. When the commandments of God are compared to the yamas and niyamas, they have an uncanny likeness.

Ten Commandments (Exodus 20)

1. You shall have no other gods before me.
2. You shall not make for yourself an image in the form of anything in heaven above or on the earth beneath or in the waters below.
3. You shall not misuse the name of the LORD your God.
4. Remember the Sabbath day by keeping it holy.
5. Honor your father and your mother.
6. You shall not murder.
7. You shall not commit adultery.
8. You shall not steal.
9. You shall not give false testimony against your neighbor.
10. You shall not covet.

Ten Yamas and Niyamas:

Yamas

1. Ahimsa: Non-harming
2. Satya: Truthfulness
3. Asteya: Responsibility (non-stealing)
4. Brahmacharya: Unity, connecting with the infinite
5. Aparigraha: Generosity

Niyamas

1. Saucha: Clarity
2. Santosha: Contentment
3. Tapas: Discipline
4. Svadyaya: Self-study
5. Ishvara pranidhara: Surrender; service to something bigger

Now let's link the Ten Commandments to the yamas and niyamas and add some Scripture to help cover the whole aspect.

Commandment 1 and ishvara pranidhana

In the first commandment, we learn that we are to place no other gods before our God, so He is to be our number one. He is the one that we must praise and worship for all His miraculous works and for how much higher His knowledge and understanding are compared to ours.

When we look at ishvara pranidhana, we see that *Ishvara* can be translated as "Supreme Being" or "God" while Pranidhana means "fixing." According to Emma Newlyn, ("Understanding the Niyamas," n.d.), this practice is about surrendering to something higher than ourselves. Pranidhana can be described as completely surrendering to our God and keeping Him at the center of our lives.

We are to place no other gods before our God, and we are to completely surrender to Him and allow Him to work in our lives.

This means that we are to have unbreakable faith, trusting God and knowing that He will lead and guide us. We surrender to Him and trust that He is our one true God and that we can rely on Him when our life feels like a roller coaster.

Both ishvara pranidhana and Commandment 1 mirror the need to have God at the very top of our priority list. In each ideology God is at the top, and we are to acknowledge, respect, and honor Him as our number one by fixating and focusing on Him and His ways.

> *Thou shalt have no other gods before me.*
> —Exodus 20:3 KJV

Commandment 2 and aparigraha

The second commandment speaks against having idols instead of God. Idols are anything that our attention is focused on more so than God. Clothes, money, pets, career, or even cars can become idols if we put them on a pedestal that is higher than God. An idol doesn't have to look like a wooden carving or a bronze statue. We can make an idol out of anything.

What causes this type of behavior in us? We become attached to material things that we can touch, hold, and see. We sometimes lose our attraction to God because we can't physically see Him, and we run instead to temporary earthly and material things to give us hope and comfort.

Aparigraha is the yama that speaks against non-attachment. When we compare Commandment 2 with aparigraha, we see that they are closely related to each other. Idols are things that we are attached to physically, emotionally, or spiritually even though we may not see the damage of holding these things at such great heights. Aparigraha is the practice of allowing material things to fade away as we pursue simplicity. We must allow the physical distractions and accumulations to become less important by releasing our attachment to them and releasing the idol mentality.

> *Their idols are silver and gold, the work of human hands. They have mouths, but do not speak; eyes, but do not see. They have ears, but do not hear; noses, but do not smell. They have hands, but do not feel; feet, but do not walk; and they do not make a sound in their throat. Those who make them become like them; so, do all who trust in them.*
> —Psalm 115:4–8 ESV

Commandment 3 and saucha

Commandment 3 is based on the purity of our hearts and minds when we use the Lord's name, and it reads, *"You shall not take the name of the* LORD *your God in vain"* (Exodus 20:7). There is much more to this commandment than we can see at first glance. It is not just about using the Lord's name along with a slew of inappropriate swear words (however, that does count), but it is also about using His name in an inappropriate way. The Hebrew word we translate as "vain" carries a meaning of empty, hollow, nothing, worthless, or to no good purpose.

When our hearts are not pure and filled with the love of the Holy Spirit, they will be filled with things that are not of the Holy Spirit. Anger, jealousy, and self-centeredness are a few of the putrid things that can make our heart turn sour.

> *For out of the heart come evil thoughts—murder, adultery, sexual immorality, theft, false testimony, slander.*
> —Matthew 15:19

Above all else, guard your heart, for everything you do flows from it.

—Proverbs 4:23

Saucha can be translated as "purity" or "cleanliness" (Shah 2019). Saucha is not just a physical cleanliness, but also a spiritual and mental cleanliness. This niyama is focused on taking care of the body by keeping up good hygiene and also having a clean area to be in (bathing, removing toxins, keeping your work area clean). The practice of saucha will encourage the mind to become uncluttered and the heart to be cleared of the things that no longer serve it but make it tainted. The practice of saucha also encourages the body to function at a higher level.

Commandment 4 and svadyaya

Remember the Sabbath day by keeping it holy.

—Exodus 20:8

So the creation of the heavens and the earth and everything in them was completed. On the seventh day God had finished his work of creation, so he rested from all of his work. And God blessed the seventh day and declared it holy, because it was the day when he rested from all his work of creation.

—Genesis 2:1–3 NLT

Even God knew the importance of self-care! He created us a mirror image of Himself.

So God created mankind in his own image, in the image of God he created them; male and female he created them.

—Genesis 1:27

So, it makes sense that we are also supposed to have a self-care routine. There are seven days in a week, and He has asked us to rest and recoup on at least day before we go out and do it all over again. He knew the importance of rest and in this commandment, He is looking out for our best interest to keep us rested through all that He wants us to accomplish during our week. But He also wants us to take time to look at ourselves from a different perspective and begin to question who we are and how we can become more like Christ. Self-improvement and self-inquiry can happen when we allow ourselves to rest from the pressures and stresses of our everyday life and week.

Rest is crucial for our self-care and well-being, and it is a gift that the Lord has blessed us with a day of rest to be still and receive renewal and to praise Him for all He has done. Self-care can be linked to self-realization once distractions are removed.

> *Examine yourselves to see whether you are in the faith. Test yourselves. Or do you not realize this about yourselves, that Jesus Christ is in you? —unless indeed you fail to meet the test!*
> —2 Corinthians 13:5 ESV

Svadyaya is the practice of self-care and self-examination as a means of enhancing the understanding of your inner self. This niyama is dedicated to the constant work of quieting your mind to get to the root of who you are. This can be achieved using meditation, reading self-help books, journaling, or incorporating a routine of sitting in the quiet and resting alone. We must seek rest in order to dig deeper into the inner programming of minds and hearts. During the week, the distraction of work, children, obligations, and commitments can pull us in many directions and cause exhaustion. It is important to put down the work spreadsheet, let the laundry sit for one more day, and do some work internally for the betterment of the mind, soul, and body.

God knows the need we have for self-care so much so that He created a commandment for us to follow. Svadyaya clearly places great importance on self-care. The Sabbath was created for us to recoup and rest which will create a routine and need for self-care. Both of these ideologies speak volumes about taking care of our bodies, minds, and souls so that we are filling our cup first before we try to fill others.

Commandment 5 and tapas

> *Honor your father and your mother.*
> —Exodus 20:12

We have all been there, the awesome teenage years (awesome according to the teenager) or the awful teenage years (awful according to the parents). In either case, parents are placed in our lives as mentors, counselors, and friends. Sometimes a parent is the person we have the hardest time get along with.

A parent has several responsibilities as their child grows and matures, and one of the most important is to discipline them so that they are aware of the morals (speech, behavior, etc.) and legal rights and laws. According to *Merriam-Webster*, the word *discipline* has several definitions; however, the one that speaks to this situation says, "To punish or penalize for the sake of enforcing obedience and perfecting moral character."

> *He who withholds his rod hates his son, But he who loves him disciplines him diligently.*
> —Proverbs 13:24 NASB

Discipline may not be an exciting topic to discuss, but if there is no discipline, there are no rules. When there are no rules, there is chaos, and with chaos comes disaster. When there is no discipline, there is chaos and mayhem; discipline is imperative for us to grow and become the best version of ourselves.

Tapas are linked to the discipline of the body, mind, and speech (Newlyn, n.d.). Tapas encourage us to consider how we speak and to discipline the words that come out of our mouths so that they are not hurtful. We are to speak truth in a loving way. Tapas also encourage us to discipline the body and not give in to harmful ways of eating that can cause addiction and cravings, but to have power over what we put in our mouths. Finally, tapas encourage discipline for the mind to lead it away from distracting thoughts so that we can think clearly without mental confusion and fog.

Commandment 6 and ahimsa

You shall not murder.
—Exodus 20:13

Repay no one evil for evil. Have regard for good things in the sight of all men. If it is possible, as much as depends on you, live peaceably with all men. Beloved, do not avenge yourselves, but rather give place to wrath; for it is written, "Vengeance is Mine, I will repay," says the Lord.
—Romans 12:17–19 NKJV

"You have heard that it was said, 'You shall love your neighbor and hate your enemy.'" But I say to you, love your enemies, bless those who curse you, do good to those who hate you, and pray for those who spitefully use you and persecute you."
—Matthew 5:43–44 NKJV

In Commandment 6, we are called to not cause pain, suffering, or murder to those around us. This applies not only in the physical sense but also in the power of the words we use. If we are condemning someone and speaking ill toward them, that is also considered to be hate and is equal to murder in the eyes of the Lord. This commandment calls for us to be lovers of others, to do good to others even when it is hard to do so, to look out for others' well-being, and to treat them with respect.

Ahimsa can be translated as "nonviolence," which is not limited to physical violence. This yama shows that we are to live in a way that is not violent to the environment, ourselves, others, or even animals. Commandment 6 and ahimsa are closely linked to each other to create harmony and peace among people, ourselves, and the environment that surrounds us all. Both ideologies encourage us to create a peaceful and loving environment for ourselves as well as others.

Commandment 7 and brahmacharya

You shall not commit adultery.
—Exodus 20:14

Adultery may be expressed as either sexual immorality (i.e., having sex with someone outside your marriage covenant) or spiritual (i.e., having idols in place of God and his authority). This commandment addresses self-control and where you are expending your energy. If you are giving into temptation and allowing adulterous thoughts to take over your life, you are succumbing to the lack of self-control and giving into the ways of the flesh instead of fighting the temptation.

Brahmacharya is the practice of moderation and using your energy in the right way instead of putting it into avenues that may cause harm to yourself and your relationships. If we allow lust to take hold in our marriage, we are opening the door for affairs and promiscuity to take hold. These behaviors not only hurt the person doing the action, but they also create a ripple effect on others who are involved in the act. But repercussions don't stop there; people who are on the sidelines are also hurt by the actions of the doers.

What does moderation mean? Moderation is the avoidance of excess or extremes, especially in one's behavior. Moderation in the use of alcohol, food, social media, sex, and so on is desirable. Self-control and moderation go hand in hand and are used to create a balanced and steady lifestyle where there is no excess ruling over the mind and body.

Commandment 8 and asteya

You shall not steal.
—Exodus 20:15

Stealing is taking something that does not rightly belong to you. Stealing may be manifest in the physical realm, but it begins in the heart when we want something that does not belong to us. We are called to be like Christ, working hard, giving generously, and trusting that the Lord Himself will provide our needs. When we steal, we are not showing our true image in God, and we are in effect telling Him that what He has provided is not good enough. God has gone before us and knows our needs before we do, so if we choose not to trust Him, we are being disobedient and ungrateful for the things He has brought to us to sustain our needs.

> *And God is able to bless you abundantly, so that in all things at all times, having all that you need, you will abound in every good work.*
> —2 Corinthians 9:8

Let the thief no longer steal, but rather let him labor, doing honest work with his own hands, so that he may have something to share with anyone in need.

—Ephesians 4:28 ESV

Asteya is non-stealing, and this term is used in the sense of all things. According to Shah (2020), this can also be looked at as stealing material, talents, relationships, gifts, achievements, successes, time, or even natural resources. When we steal, we feel like we are lacking in an area of our lives and become selfish, greedy, and jealous of what others may have.

Asteya can also be in the form of stealing joy from the present moment by worrying about the future or being stuck in the past. It is allowing the present moment to be taken away by things that are not in our control.

Therefore do not be anxious about tomorrow, for tomorrow will be anxious for itself. Sufficient for the day is its own trouble.

—Matthew 6:34 ESV

Stop dwelling on past events and brooding over times gone by. I am doing something new; it's springing up—can't you see it? I am making a road in the desert, rivers in the wasteland.

—Isaiah 43:18–19 CJB

Commandment 9 and satya

You shall not give false testimony against your neighbor.

—Exodus 20:16

False testimony can also be viewed as lying, and this is one of the sins that God condemns throughout the Bible. Lying is not in His nature, as His word is the truth, the way, and the life. Lies undermine the character of God's people by sowing distrust and dishonesty among them. In the end, lying leads to arguments, violence, and isolation. Jesus speaks of the enemy as the father of lies, and we can see that the first lie was told in the very beginning in the Garden of Eden when the serpent lied to Eve about the fruit on the tree.

> *Then the serpent said to the woman, "You will not surely die. For God knows that in the day you eat of it your eyes will be opened, and you will be like God, knowing good and evil."*
> —Genesis 3:4–5 NKJV

> *You are of your father the devil, and the desires of your father you want to do. He was a murderer from the beginning, and does not stand in the truth, because there is no truth in him. When he speaks a lie, he speaks from his own resources, for he is a liar and the father of it.*
> —John 8:44 NKJV

The last yama is called satya, and it is the one that relates to truthfulness. Satya encompasses a lifestyle of living for truth, being honest in your speech and actions, and having the dignity and integrity of an honest life. Commandment 9 and satya are mirror concepts when boiled down to the main idea, which has to do with honesty and integrity and being a truthful and trustworthy person on whom others can rely.

Commandment 10 and santosha

You shall not covet your neighbor's house. You shall not covet your neighbor's wife, or his male or female servant, his ox or donkey, or anything that belongs to your neighbor.

—Exodus 20:17

You desire and do not have, so you murder. You covet and cannot obtain, so you fight and quarrel. You do not have, because you do not ask. You ask and do not receive, because you ask wrongly, to spend it on your passions.

—James 4:2–3 ESV

Coveting is wanting and desiring something that does not belong to us, and it causes havoc inside our hearts that can lead to destructive behavior toward others. This commandment can be closely linked to commandment 8, which forbids stealing from others. Commandment 10 is more about being content with what the Lord has given instead of coveting, wishing, and desiring the things that the Lord has given to those around us. The heart can become so enveloped in wishing for what others have that we get lost in "what ifs" and thinking, "I must have that to be happy" that we miss the blessing of what we have been provided.

Santosha can be described as contentment, which is the definition of not coveting. The idea behind santosha is to be grateful for what we have and not allow ourselves to become jealous of what others have. We try to be happy with what we have and eliminate the tendency to think, "I would be so much happier if I had . . . " That is, we should accept what we have and who we are so that we believe we are enough and what we have is enough (e.g., physical possessions, career, money, kids, disciplines, etc.).

As we read in Scripture, God created everything; it was all in His hands. *"Through him all things were made; without him nothing was made that has been made"* (John 1:3).

So, if the Lord created it, then He has control over what is happening, not us. However, the things He creates can become polluted with false methodologies, idols, and falsehoods. Some Christians are leery of yoga because of the origination of the practice and because the poses or asanas are named after deities or gods in the east.

The practice of yoga is healthy for our mind, body, and spirit. It is pure. But when submerged in the pollution of false methodologies, yoga becomes polluted. Anything pure, whether it be an object or a person or an ideology, will become tainted if submerged in something that is polluted.

Let's think of it as a teabag or ball of tea leaves. First, consider the water in which the tea will be brewed. Any number of variables related to the water (the mineral content, the source of the water, the pH or freshness) may affect the quality of the tea.

If we use a water source that is high in minerals (e.g., magnesium, sodium, potassium, and phosphorus), the tea will be darker in color and more prone to water that has limescale in it However, if we use distilled water, the tea will be bland due to the lack of minerals in it.

Where did the water come from? Is it from the tap, filtered, or bottled? This also makes a difference in the taste of the water and the mineral content. Typically, a good cup of tea has a neutral pH level (as close to 7 as possible). If the tea is too acidic, it will be bitter, and if the tea is too high on the alkaline scale, it will be dull.

The amount of time that the water has been sitting out is also a factor. The longer the water you use to brew the tea has been sitting out, the less oxygen it has in it; The best tea comes from water that is full of oxygen because it brings out the flavors at a higher level.

There are a lot of factors that can make tea taste bitter or vibrant, which makes the water a crucial component. Next, let's look at the tea type, temperature, and the amount of time we need to steep the tea. The table below breaks down several types of tea and various ranges for temperature and brewing time (artfultea. com, n.d.). These aspects can make tea taste bland, bitter, sour, spicy, earthy, floral, fruity or even sweet.

Tea Type	Temperature	Time
Black	212 degrees	3–5 minutes
Green	175–180 degrees	1–2 minutes
White	175–180 degrees	2–3 minutes
Oolong	195 degrees	2–3 minutes
Purple	175–180 degrees	3 minutes
Herbal	212 degrees	5–10 minutes
Rooibos	212 degrees	5–10 minutes

What if we put our tea bag or leaves in a cup that had been sitting out on the sidewalk all day and steeped our tea in that for 20 minutes at 250 degrees? Can you imagine the awful taste from the polluted water, wrong temperature, and excessive time? The tea would smell awful; it would be burnt, making it bitter and hard to drink.

What if we were to put our tea bag or leaves in a cup of clean, freshly poured water at the appropriate temperature and for the optimum amount of time? The tea would come out with its highest potential and flavor bursting at the seams.

The environment needs to be unpolluted in order to result in an excellent final product. Similarly, we cannot put yoga in a polluted environment and expect it to produce good fruits. When we set the stage for yoga in a Christian environment, we can see the positive aspects of how the practice can make you a healthier individual.

Self-Inquiry

In your life, what is something that may have been polluted by your surroundings? Think about your social life, work environment, children, family, or marriage. What are some things that you can adjust the settings on to improve the end result?

What to Pray

> *Whoever walks with the wise becomes wise, but the companion of fools will suffer harm.*
> —Proverbs 13:20 ESV

> *Blessed is the man who walks not in the counsel of the wicked, nor stands in the way of sinners, nor sits in the seat of scoffers; but his delight is in the law of the LORD, and on his law, he meditates day and night. He is like a tree planted by streams of water that yields its fruit in its season, and its leaf does not wither. In all that he does, he prosers. The wicked are not so, but the chaff that the wind drives them away.*
> —Psalm 1:1–4 ESV

Digging Deeper

Read Matthew 13:1–23. How can we relate the seed parable to the idea of the art of making tea?

REFLECTION

I AM ENOUGH

Maybe I wasn't enough for that friendship.
Maybe I wasn't enough for that job.
Maybe I wasn't enough for that marriage.
Maybe I wasn't enough as a parent.
Maybe I wasn't enough as a daughter.
Maybe . . .

The list can go on and on detailing ways in which we might think about not being enough. If I were to ask you to name three things you like about yourself and three things you don't like, which would be easier for you to come up with?

You know who else felt not-good enough? Moses!

He had a stuttering problem, and the Lord still used him to bring freedom to the Israelites. He worked through Moses even though his speech issue made him feel not good enough. He worked through his weaknesses. He also used Aaron to speak for Moses. Sometimes, He sends us help to cover our weaknesses.

But what does the Apostle Paul say that will help us combat the lies of insecurity, weakness, and not being enough?

But he said to me, "My grace is sufficient for you, for my power is made perfect in weakness." Therefore I

will boast all the more gladly about my weaknesses, so that Christ's power may rest on me.
—2 Corinthians 12:9

I wear my heart on my sleeve and when I get hurt, I withdraw into isolation. Thank God for His sweet pushes to make me more able to express my feelings. He is strong when I am weak. For instance, I am not skilled at handling the money and business aspects of my studio. Sometimes, when we are weak, He sends someone (such as my wonderful husband, Cody) to help us along the way. The person He sends to you may be someone that is comparable to Aaron.

You are enough. You are chosen and not overlooked. You are His. And He says that you are enough. He says that when you are weak, He will be your strength. When you are weeping, He will be your joy. When you doubt, He will be your confidence. When you are hurting, He will bind up your wounds. When you feel like you are not enough, He is enough and more to carry you through.

Believe His truth about you: You are enough because I am lives in you. What others say about you does not compare to what He says about you. Grab ahold of God's truth; you are enough.

CHAPTER TWO

TAKING CARE OF THE BODY
THAT HOUSES THE HOLY SPIRIT

Do you not know that your bodies are temples of the Holy Spirit, who is in you, whom you have received from God? You are not your own; you were bought at a price. Therefore honor God with your bodies.

—1 Corinthians 6:19–20

Don't you know that you yourselves are God's temple and that God's Spirit dwells in your midst? If anyone destroys God's temple, God will destroy that person; for God's temple is sacred, and you together are that temple.

—1 Corinthians 3:16–17

Suppose that one of your closest friends, let's call her Mary, calls and invites you over for dinner one evening. You are excited because you have not been to Mary's house before, and you are thrilled to have been invited someplace new. As you open the front door, a wall of stench hits you in the face. Not just a regular stench but one that smells like the time you went to the city dump to drop off some large pieces of furniture. The smell is a mixture of cigarette smoke, dirty laundry, filthy animals, and possibly a hint of fish that was left out for two weeks. It is so potent that it nearly knocked you back down the stairs and onto the sidewalk. But, for the sake of not hurting Mary's feelings, you decide to venture further into the house to sit with your friend.

As you make your way through the front door, you notice that there is a small pathway carved out through the middle of the room. The room is filled with boxes, dirty clothes, old children's toys, blankets, and trash; there is just enough space for one person to walk on the path to get to the kitchen.

As you make it to the kitchen, you see that the kitchen sink is full of dirty dishes with food particles left on them, and you think you might see bugs crawling on the countertops and on the mountain of dishes. You start to take a seat at what you think resembles a table (you aren't too sure because of all the mail and garbage on top), but as you pull out a chair to sit down, you notice a large pile of feline vomit in the seat.

Need we go on? The house is unkept and unclean.

- How comfortable are you in this situation?
- How likely are you to stay for an extended time?

According to the Scriptures in the beginning of this chapter, our bodies house the Holy Spirit and if we aren't taking care of the body He has given us, we are allowing the Holy Spirit to dwell in dirt and disaster. We are allowing someone of such importance to sit and dwell in the unkept and unclean parts of our bodies.

What can we do to be considered bad stewards of our bodies? There are multiple ways to mistreat your body and a few that stick out the most are drunkenness, gluttony, sloth, and greed.

Drunkenness

> *Do not get drunk on wine, which leads to debauchery.*
> *Instead be filled with the Spirit.*
>
> —Ephesians 5:18

> *The acts of the flesh are obvious: sexual immorality,*
> *impurity and debauchery; idolatry and witchcraft;*
> *hatred, discord, jealousy, fits of rage, selfish ambition,*
> *dissensions, factions and envy; drunkenness, orgies,*
> *and the like. I warn you, as I did before, that those*
> *who live like this will not inherit the kingdom of God.*
>
> —Galatians 5:19–21

> *Be alert and of sober mind. Your enemy the devil prowls*
> *around like a roaring lion looking for someone to devour.*
>
> —1 Peter 5:8

We have either seen excess drinking in person or portrayed on a television show; it can look like an exhilarating and exciting time, but it can take a turn for the worst and cause a person to end up in a bad place. When we allow ourselves to drink too much and become intoxicated, there are repercussions. Alcohol slows down the areas of the brain that control body movements, which causes slurred speech and blurry vision. It can also affect our moods and actions. When we are under the influence of alcohol, we are not ourselves, and we tend to make poor decisions that can harm others as well as ourselves.

Gluttony

> *Do not join those who drink too much wine or gorge*
> *themselves on meat, for drunkards and gluttons*
> *become poor, and drowsiness clothes them in rags.*
>
> —Proverbs 23:20–21

Gluttony will take a toll on our bodies and minds if we allow it to consume us. When we allow gluttony to overtake us, we are at risk of destroying our health by promoting excess body fat. Overeating can disrupt your body's natural response to hunger by throwing off the hormones involved in alerting the body when you are ready to eat.

Sloth

> *A sluggard's appetite is never filled, but the desires of the diligent are fully satisfied.*
>
> —Proverbs 13:4

> *How long will you lie there, you sluggard? When will you get up from your sleep?*
>
> —Proverbs 6:9

Slothfulness or laziness can create physical problems that may range from gaining weight to having overly tight muscles that make it difficult to move. It can also create chemical imbalances in your brain that cause anxiety and depression. Get up and move your body in some way and see how you feel after you finish. Your body movements will feel more fluid, and you will get a dose of endorphins, which will stimulate your happy chemicals.

Greed

> *Then he said to them, "Watch out! Be on your guard against all kinds of greed; life does not consist in an abundance of possessions."*
>
> —Luke 12:15

> *The greedy stir up conflict, but those who trust in the* LORD *will prosper.*
>
> —Proverbs 28:25

Greed can take an honest person and turn them into a manipulator—someone determined to get what they want without worrying about who they hurt or how they fulfill those desires. Being greedy can be a person's trauma response to not having enough when they were younger, and it can become a survival tactic.

Yoga helps keep your body healthy and functioning the way God created it to function. There is always a "why" to each pose, and yoga has a long list of benefits that can encompass areas of your body's muscular, skeletal, endocrinal, lymphatic, and digestive systems. Yoga has been shown to help calm the nervous system, reduce the effects of post-traumatic stress disorder (PTSD), encourage breathing to help bring more oxygen to the blood and body, build strength, and increase flexibility.

For example, when you lie on your back and bring the right knee in toward your chest, you are stimulating the ascending colon, when you switch sides and pull the left knee in toward your chest, you are pressing on the descending colon. This is called the wind-relieving pose, and it helps to move your digestive system around in a natural and non-medicated way while toning muscles in the abdominal wall. From this pose, there are several benefits that are designed to help the body.

Try another pose. For this pose you can slip a block underneath your lower back and put your legs up in the air. You also have the option to scoot close to the nearest wall and lie down while putting your legs up against the wall. This pose (called "legs up the wall") is used to improve circulation in the feet and legs as well as to help lower your heart rate and reduce anxiety.

These are just two of the yoga poses designed to help our bodies function optimally and to help us heal our bodies instead of leaning only on pharmaceuticals.

Self-Inquiry

What are some things that prevent us from being good stewards to house the Holy Spirit?

What to Pray

> *Therefore, I urge you, brothers and sisters, in view of God's mercy, to offer your bodies as a living sacrifice, holy and pleasing to God—this is your true and proper worship.*
> *—Romans 12:1*

> *No, I strike a blow to my body and make it my slave so that after I have preached to others, I myself will not be disqualified for the prize.*
>
> —1 Corinthians 9:27

Digging Deeper

Can you commit to being a better steward for one week? What can you eliminate or add to your schedule to become a healthier steward for the Holy Spirit?

BROKEN GLASS

The beautiful thing is that we are all like broken glass. We all have brokenness inside of us, and it can come in all shapes and sizes, sharp or dull, thick or thin.

It doesn't matter how big your broken glass pieces are. Some of our pieces may be thick and some thin, some bigger and others smaller, and some may be jagged and sharp, while other pieces are smooth and safe to touch because the edges are dulled down. God sees all our brokenness the same. He doesn't judge us but guides us into healing. You see, broken glass is still broken glass regardless of its size.

But beware that newly broken glass shards are sharp and dangerous and should be handled with care. In much the same way, beware that, in the beginning stages of emotional healing, we are especially sensitive to things that may remind us of the hurt. As a result, we tend to avoid the broken places because they are dangerous or painful and need to be handled with care.

Think about the last time you were broken by something or someone. Recall how badly the hurt would sting when it was discussed or brought up casually and how each time someone got too close to your wound, you pulled away or steered clear of addressing it.

Now think about a dull piece of glass, one that is older and has been weathered. The edges aren't so scary and sharp; they are smooth and beautifully worn. Being a visual learner, I envision sea glass as an example. Sea glass is tossed around the sea and smoothed out by the waves. After a while with some time, prayer, friendship, love, grace, mercy patience, God wears down those sharp edges of your broken pieces. They don't hurt as much as they did in the beginning. They become less dangerous to handle because they aren't as sharp.

The Lord will use your broken pieces to glorify Himself and create something beautiful if you let Him. Let Him guide you to your healing; let Him guide you to those who can help dull those sharp edges. He places these people in your life to work with you to take the sting out of the sharpness of those glass shards.

He heals the brokenhearted and binds up their wounds.
—Psalm 147:3

The LORD is close to the brokenhearted and saves those who are crushed in spirit.
—Psalm 34:18

But he said to me, "My grace is sufficient for you for my power is made perfect in weakness." Therefore I will boast all the more gladly about my weaknesses, so that Christ's power may rest on me.
—2 Corinthians 12:9

Show your brokenness to others so they can see how the Lord has worked through you.

CHAPTER THREE
MIND, BODY, AND SPIRIT –
3 IN 1

One of the reasons I practice yoga is because of how it benefits my mind, body, and spirit. Earlier, we covered some of the physical benefits that yoga can offer you; we will cover a few more of those as well as what the Bible says about mind and spirit health.

While I was praying one morning, the Lord gave me an insightful and exciting vision of how our bodies can be compared to three in one, just as we see in the Trinity. We are composed of three parts: bones, fascia, and skin. (I love fascia, I am fascinated with our anatomy). Applying the concepts of the Holy Trinity, we can look at our bodies in a different way.

God is our main source of support; He is the one who holds everything together—comparable to the function of our bones. Jesus is the piece that holds us all together; He is our fascia, the one that helps us move and act. The Holy Spirit is our protector, guide, and intuition. He is our skin that keeps our vital organs and bones covered and safe.

If we didn't have bones we could not stand, could not eat, could not move; we would be a puddle on the ground. With no protection for our organs, we would be little more than a human jellyfish.

Fascia is important to our bodies because it enables the bones in the skeleton to move, allows the heart to beat, gives us shape, and holds us together (think of fascia as a thick elastic band). If we didn't have fascia our body movements would stop, our heart would stop, and our digestive tract could not function.

What would happen if we didn't have skin? All our muscles would move out of placement; our organs could move and dislodge, and our bones would be exposed. Germs and toxins could freely enter our bodies and create infections and illnesses more easily and without much interference. Our muscles would become dehydrated, and our body fluids would evaporate.

What Does Yoga Do for Your Mind?

We have all felt the gripping effects of anxiety and/or depression at one point or another—the tightening of the chest, short breaths, sweaty palms, the shaky voice, and tears that flow during an anxiety attack. Anxiety is future-based; it wants us to step into the future of what-ifs and maybes in order to get us away from the present moment. If we are in the present moment and can find an anchor to ground us and keep us steady, anxiety loses. Yoga helps us become more aware and better at anchoring our minds to the "right now."

Where are you right now? Take a moment to access your surroundings, take note of how you feel, and begin to bring yourself into the present moment. If you have not practiced grounding before, it may feel strange to you to slow down, but it might look something like this.

Right now:

- *I feel my feet steadily pressing into the floor as I am sitting in a chair.*
- *I notice my thighs and my back are being supported by the chair and in this moment, I can breathe.*
- *I know that for this present moment, I am safe, and I can control my breath.*

Depression is not just about sadness and being bummed out. Gary Kraftsow notes that depression and related emotions are "characterized by a loss of energy, appetite, interest, and enthusiasm and are marked by a slowing down of the body's metabolic rate" (Kraftsow, 2023).

Depression colors all aspects of our lives, making everything less enjoyable, less interesting, less important, less lovable, and less worthwhile. Depression saps our energy; motivation; and ability to experience joy, pleasure, excitement, anticipation, satisfaction, connection, and meaning. In the midst of depression, all your thresholds tend to be lower. You're more impatient, quicker to anger and get frustrated, quicker to break down, and it takes you longer to bounce back from everything (Winch 2015).

> *Do not conform to the pattern of this world, but be transformed by the renewing of your mind. Then you will be able to test and approve what God's will is—his good, pleasing and perfect will.*
> —Romans 12:2

> *Therefore do not worry about tomorrow, for tomorrow will worry about itself. Each day has enough trouble of its own.*
> —Matthew 6:34

Say to those who have an anxious heart, "Be strong; fear not! Behold, your God will come with vengeance, with the recompense of God. He will come and save you."
—Isaiah 35:4 ESV

What Does Yoga Do for Your Body?

A better question would be, "What doesn't yoga do for your body?" Yoga works to improve muscle tone and flexibility; increase blood flow and circulation; and build strength for joints, ligaments, tendons, and muscles.

Dear friend, I pray that you may enjoy good health and that all may go well with you, even as your soul is getting along well.
—3 John 2

What Does Yoga Do for Your Soul?

Our bodies are longing for stillness, for a sense of peace and calm in a place where there is no hurry or deadline. Busy has become the newest way to describe our lives; busy has become a prominent lifestyle, and anxiety is a byproduct of it. Once we slow down, we can feel what is happening in our bodies and monitor our breath; then we are able to put the practice of busy down for that moment. Our souls are being pulled in a million directions as to how we should feel about every aspect of our lives. Yoga can offer you the stillness to just be with yourself and access how you are feeling and what your thoughts are; then from a calm place, you can make steady and stronger decisions.

Be still before the LORD and wait patiently for him.
—Psalm 37:7

Self-Inquiry

How often do you implement exercise for your mind, body, and spirit? Are you going to church, joining life groups, or getting your cup filled in order to fill others? What do you do to fill your cup in these areas?

What to Pray

- **Mind:**

    "Love the LORD your God with all your heart and with all your soul and with all you mind and with all your strength."

    —Mark 12:30

- **Body:**

    "The LORD sustains them on their sickbed and restores them from their bed of illness."

    —Psalm 41:3

- **Spirit:**

    "For those who live according to the flesh set their mind on the things of the flesh, but those who live according to the spirit, the things of the spirit. For to be carnally minded is death, but to be spiritually minded is life and peace."

    —Romans 8:5–6 NKJV

- **All 3 in 1:**

    "Now may the God of peace himself sanctify you completely, and may your whole spirit and soul and body be kept blameless at the coming of our Lord Jesus Christ."

    —1 Thessalonians 5:23 ESV

Digging Deeper

While doing any form of exercise this week, can you create a deeper connection with God? In your moments of alone time, you can cultivate a meaningful conversation with our sweet Lord. While exercising, you could recite this Scripture: *"Draw near to God, and he will draw near to you* (James 4:8 ESV).

WHO ARE YOUR AARON AND HUR?

The Amalekites came and attacked the Israelites at Rephidim. Moses said to Joshua, "Choose some of our men and go out to fight the Amalekites. Tomorrow I will stand on top of the hill with the staff of God in my hands." So Joshua fought the Amalekites as Moses had ordered, and Moses, Aaron and Hur went to the top of the hill. As long as Moses held up his hands, the Israelites were winning, but whenever he lowered his hands, the Amalekites were winning. When Moses' hands grew tired, they took a stone and put it under him, and he sat on it. Aaron and Hur held his hands up—one on one side, one on the other—so that his hands remained steady till sunset. So Joshua overcame the Amalekite army with the sword.

—Exodus 17:8–13

Who was Hur? He was a companion of Moses. Who was Aaron? He was Moses' brother. Moses had a job to do. We all have a job just as important as Moses. Life can knock us down, and we can all get tired of doing what we have been called to do.

God knew that life would be difficult; he didn't say *if*; He said "when" troubles of any kind come your way (James 1:2). He gives us companions to help us along the way as we read in Scripture: *"Two are better than one, because they have a good return for their labor: If either of them falls down, one can help the other up. But pity anyone who falls and has no one to help them up"* (Ecclesiastes 4:9–10).

Small groups in church, work, and friendship circles are crucial to our health and well-being. There will be days when we can't stand on our own two feet, when we need people who love us to help us stand.

Some days we will be Moses; some days we will be Aaron or Hur. God has placed you in the role you are in right now to either be the one leading or the one uplifting and encouraging.

CHAPTER FOUR

PATIENCE WITH STRETCHING AND PATIENCE WITH THE PROMISES OF THE LORD

It is easy for me to get lost on Instagram, Facebook, Tik Tok, and Pinterest. I start looking at pictures innocently—just to pass a bit of time and drift away for a moment. But it is never only for a moment before some flashy yoga picture catches my eye, and I get caught up in the awe of the picture and how perfect it all seems. I know that those photos can be edited on a computer to make the participant's body look extraordinary and to make the pose look almost perfect. But I look and then comes the comparison, jealousy, and envy of the pose and the person.

"How come I can't do that yet?"

"Her leg goes where?"

"How on earth can she make it look so effortless?"

It doesn't have to be a yoga pose. Maybe you want to create that ultra special cake that you saw on your favorite baker's Instagram, but yours didn't turn out quite like the picture. We must stop comparing ourselves with the people behind the social media accounts, start asking ourselves different questions, and let go of the need for instant gratification.

"How long have they been working on opening their body to get to where they are now?"

"What does their practice routine look like?"

"What have they endured to get to this point in their lives?"

Practice and patience. And a whole lot of both.

> *We do not want you to become lazy, but to imitate those who through faith and patience inherit what has been promised.*
> —Hebrews 6:12

With yoga, this scenario can be linked to our patience with the Lord and His promises. Throughout the Bible, the Lord has given promises of love, faith, and protection to his children. What about promises that He has given you specifically? When I pray for words at the beginning of the year, I wait patiently for Him to tell me because those are the words I use to hold onto the promises He has in store for me. Below are a few words He has given me in previous years along some reflections on what happened that year.

2020	Joy	My father died; the pandemic hit; we were afraid of losing the studio.
2021	Relentless	We were experiencing the aftermath of the pandemic (fear), and the studio was suffering financially. The Lord urged me to go into the nearby city of Mineral Wells, and open a second studio location. He provided the space, the instructors, and the finances.
2022	Overcomer	We didn't think there was a way for us to move into a bigger space in Weatherford. He provided the finances and the location; He led us to where we are now after we were asked to leave our previous location.

2023	Rest	This has been a year of taking a step back and allowing my body to rest. He wants me to take the moments of rest and cherish them.

"For I know the plans I have for you," declares the LORD,
*"plans to prosper you and not to harm you, plans to
give you hope and a future."* —Jeremiah 29:11

Another great biblical example of patience and promises is found in Joseph's story. Joseph started off as his father's favorite (was given an extraordinary coat). He was given strong visions and dreams; however, this made his brothers jealous and angry. After he shared his vision with his brothers, they plotted to kill him, but he was sold into slavery and lived with Potiphar instead. He had found favor with Potiphar who made Joseph his assistant and put him in charge of his household, trusting him with everything he owned. Disaster struck as Potiphar's wife wanted more from Joseph than he was willing to give, and after Joseph turned her down, she claimed that he had attacked her to sleep with her. After the false claim was told to Potiphar, he was angry and put Joseph in prison. Again, the Lord was with Joseph, and he found favor in the prison with the guards who soon put him in charge of things there.

Joseph began interpreting dreams in the dungeon and interpreted a dream for the pharaoh's cupbearer. The interpretation came to fruition, and the cupbearer remembered Joseph two years after he helped him. When the pharaoh needed a dream interpreted, Joseph was called to help. Joseph interpreted the pharaoh's dream, and he was then put in charge of Egypt. There was a great famine in the land and Joseph's brothers were forced to go to Egypt to ask for grain. They were forced to ask the brother that they had betrayed to help save their lives. Joseph helped them and gave us this Scripture to hold onto:

> *"As for you, you meant evil against me, but God meant it for good, to bring it about that many people should be kept alive, as they are today."*
> —Genesis 50:20 ESV

This story teaches us that when God gives us a promise, He always fulfills it. We may go through trials like the hills on a roller coaster (and maybe even get a little queasy from all the twists and turns), but we still end up where He wants us to.

> *Let us not become weary in doing good, for at the proper time we will reap a harvest if we do not give up.*
> —Galatians 6:9

During the time we are working toward our promises or our poses/stretching, growth is happening. We may not see it each day, but it just takes one step to get closer to the goal. Learning and stretching are happening so that when our promises come to fruition, we will be ready, able, and wise enough to handle what comes with the promises. In the meantime, we are to wait patiently for the Lord's promises and stretching. In doing so, we should avoid these pitfalls:

- **Going too far too quickly.** This goes back to seeking instant gratification. That is, we want things to happen right away, and we typically don't want to work for them or wait around for things to happen. You cannot become insanely flexible and strong in one night. Nor can you "make" the Lord's promises come true by pushing things faster. You must take your time (seek stillness), listen to your body (Lord), and practice regularly outside the studio/gym/classroom (not only on Sundays for church).

Do not be anxious about anything, but in every situation, by prayer and petition, with thanksgiving, present your requests to God.

—Philippians 4:6

- **Being inconsistent.** Let's say you see something you want to work toward and start the process, but you get tired after not seeing results right away, so you quit. You need to press into the Lord and check in with Him consistently so you can start to see what direction He wants you to go to make those promises to come to life.

- **Using funky routines.** Set yourself up for success. If you want to work toward your poses and those promise, there are a few ways to keep a regular routine to max out your time. When comparing stretching and promises, there are a few things that mirror each other regarding a typical church service and the routine you should follow to stretch.

Stretching	Lord's Promises
Do a warm-up and get your blood and body ready for movement	Worship to get your heart in the right place and your mind free of clutter and distractions.
Establish a routine or plan of action for the day to get the results you are seeking.	Dig deeper into the Word for a longer period (i.e., sermon at church).
After you finish any kind of workout, you should do some static stretching (poses held for an extended period).	Pray. Pray for an extended period. Our church has a gathering twice a year called "21 Days of Prayer." It is a dedicated time for us to carve out a chunk of our day and pray.

Self-Inquiry:

Is there a promise you have been waiting to be fulfilled? Have you grown weary of waiting, and have you tried to force it to happen?

What to Pray

> *When you pass through the waters, I will be with you; and when you pass through the rivers, they will not sweep over you. When you walk through the fire, you will not be burned; the flames will not set you ablaze.*
> —Isaiah 43:2

> *Be still before the* LORD *and wait patiently for him.*
> —Psalm 37:7

Digging Deeper

Take time to write out the promises that the Lord has given you and pray over your list. Have there been any changes or advancements to get you closer to those promises? It doesn't matter how small the change or advancement is, He is moving you closer to your promise!

REFLECTION
WHAT IF GOD SAYS "NO" OR "WAIT"?

The Rolling Stones have a famous song, "You Can't Always Get What You Want," that speaks to a deep truth about "unanswered" prayer. The lyrics talk about knowing that there will be times in your life when you do not get what you *want*. But with patience and perseverance, you will often find that you get exactly what you *need*.

Here's an example of how this principle works. We prayed and prayed for our sweet cat Louie to come home. Every day after he went missing, we went outside and eagerly looked for him to be on the back porch. But he was nowhere to be found. I was so upset and confused, especially because of my daughter Kendal's reaction and disappointment that it broke my heart. She had such a deep love for that cat, and I couldn't understand why God would take him away from her. Do I miss him? Yes! But I must trust God enough to hold my little girl's tender heart. I must trust Him to ease her sadness and show her that when we are sad or doubtful, we pray.

I thought I could hold Kendal's heart better than He could. I thought I could teach her about the power of prayer. But God is teaching her how to handle disappointment. He is teaching her how to ask Him the hard questions and trust that God has her in His best interests. He is teaching her to trust Him even when it hurts. He is molding her and me through these times to strengthen our faith in Him to always hope even when it hurts.

May the God of hope fill you with all joy and peace as
you trust in him, so that you may overflow with hope
by the power of the Holy Spirit.
—Romans 15:13

"For I know the plans I have for you," declares the Lord,
"plans to prosper you and not to harm you, plans to
give you hope and a future."
—Jeremiah 29:11

We continued to pray for Louie's safe return, and then the Lord started working on another one of my prayer requests instead of bringing Louie home. The Lord had shown me that He wanted me to build a studio in Mineral Wells, Texas, about 20 minutes from our current home studio. I had asked for one thing (Louie's safe return), and He answered another prayer instead (the location for my studio). He was blessing me with the growth and expansion of the studio to reach more people for Him.

What should we do when God's answers to our prayers are silent or nonexistent?

- Check your faith.
  And without faith it is impossible to please God,
  because anyone who comes to him must believe that
  he exists and that he rewards those who earnestly
  seek him.
  —Hebrews 11:6

- Check your ask.
  This is the confidence we have in approaching God:
  that if we ask anything according to his will, he hears
  us. And if we know that he hears us—whatever we

ask—we know that we have what we asked of him.
—1 John 5:14–15

- Check your why.
  Search me, God, and know my heart; test me and know my anxious thoughts. See if there is any offensive way in me, and lead me in the way everlasting.
  —Psalm 139:23–24

If you check all the boxes and know that your motives are pure, but your prayer goes unanswered, put your trust in God because He has your best interest in mind. He sees the whole picture, and He holds each piece; it all comes down to trusting Him.

CHAPTER FIVE
REPETITION OF PRAYER AND REPETITION OF POSES

The definition of insanity is doing the same thing over and over again but expecting different results.

—Albert Einstein

The Power of Repetitious Prayer

We pray to the Lord and give Him our needs, requests, and thanksgiving. This act of communication can sometimes become a process that is repetitive and mundane. A conversation that is thoughtless and emotionless is not what our Father wants from us or for us.

Think about the last time you had a conversation with someone you loved deeply (maybe a spouse, child, relative, coworker, mentor) and see if it mirrors the conversations that you have with God.

Hi,

Did you see what Stella said and did to me? I am so upset and angry about her actions, I just don't even know what to say or do. I want to see her pay for what she did to me! My husband is so lazy and narcissistic, and I need him to back away a little bit. And these kids? Where do I even start with how hormonal and argumentative, they have all been. I need to win the lottery, have God change my husband and my kids, and then buy a plane and fly away to an island where no one knows my name.

We say all this to the recipient in one breath with no time for them to answer us or offer sympathy or advice. Phew! That's a lot of complaining all in one breath. Now think about your prayer life or the last time you sat down and prayed earnestly. Does this example sound familiar to you? Often, we come to God with our complaints and venting and neglect to praise Him. Or even worse, we don't leave time for Him to speak to us, so we are basically demanding things and praying *at* Him not *to* Him.

Let's try to reword this example as a prayer:

Lord,
My heart is hurting because Stella and I had a massive argument, I am praying that You will let me see the light in this situation and that You will convict my heart about what happened on my end so that I can make things right. Thank You for allowing Stella to be in my life, and I am praying that we can get things straightened out. Thank You for my husband; we may not see eye to eye all the time, but I know that he loves me. Look inside my heart and see what I need to adjust in order to love him well. Lord, You know my love for my children

and that I am thankful for them, but sometimes, I get overwhelmed and emotional and lose my temper with them. Please give me the patience I need and help me to apologize to them when I am wrong. I am praying for financial stability in my home and my business, and it wouldn't hurt to win the lottery. Thank You for all You are doing and have done for me and my family.

What a huge difference in heart posture and communication this is. If you are currently praying like the first example, it doesn't mean that you are wrong; it just means that your heart could use some practice in prayer.

God does not want us to pray using the same words or phrases over and over; when we do that, our prayers lose meaning and power. Prayer is a form of communication with our Father, one in which we are honest and bring forth all our needs but ask Him to help us see where we could have done better or where He can make us better. Look back at the first example and remember that the Lord wants you to come to Him with praise, thanksgiving, and needs.

> When you pray, don't babble on and on as the gentiles do. They think their prayers are answered merely by repeating their words again and again.
> —Matthew 6:7 NLT

If our prayers are thoughtless and emotionless due to a lack of sincerity and a need to complain, it is time to reassess our motives for prayer. Empty phrases can translate into vain repetition and babbling.

Jesus gave us the Lord's Prayer in Matthew 6:9–13 (KJV) as a model:

> *Our Father, which art in heaven, Hallowed be thy name.*
> *Thy kingdom come, Thy will be done, in earth as it is*
> *in heaven.*
> *Give us this day our daily bread.*
> *And forgive us our debts, as we forgive our debtors.*
> *And lead us not into temptation, but deliver us from*
> *evil: For thine is the kingdom, and the power, and the*
> *glory, for ever. Amen.*

This is a guideline—the bare bones—or the skeleton of prayer that underlies the rest of what we want to say when we enter into prayer with the Lord. This model prayer will get you started by thanking the Lord and asking for His protection throughout your day. If you prayed only this prayer every day, would you have a deep connection with the Lord and what you are saying, or would you just be going through the motions? Talk to Him. Show Him you are confident and pay attention to what you are saying. There is power in your prayer. He knows what you need; just talk to Him about it. There is also power in the consistency of your prayers.

I started a yoga studio in 2016 and when I look back at the prayers in my journals, I see that I have continually prayed for God to use the studios to reach the lost and hurting. I have also prayed for financial success to help them stay afloat so that we can continue to do His work. He hasn't failed in providing the finances or the people that need us over the years, and He won't stop now. This is a persistent prayer that I pray every day, and He never fails to amaze us with His results. This not only makes my heart rely on Him and His promises, but it builds trust in and dependence on the Lord.

- *"Pray continually"* (1 Thessalonians 5:17).
- *"Then Jesus told his disciples a parable to show them that they should always pray and not give up."* (Luke 18:1)

The Importance of Routine and Repetition in Yoga

Baron Baptiste founded Baptiste yoga, which has 53 poses linked with breath and movement. When I first found this style of yoga, I was knocked off my feet. The temperature inside the studio was 90-degrees plus with humidity; we were constantly moving, and the class was challenging. I had found the piece of my life that had been missing, and I connected to this practice on more than one level.

Baptiste yoga follows a specific sequence, or bare bones, in order to warm the body appropriately to avoid injury and open the areas of the body that need to be opened before attempting the "apex pose" of the sequence. The apex pose is generally a variety of backbends practiced in the sequence. A backbend is where the front of the body extends, and the spine is moving backward. Wheel pose or Urdhva Dhanurasana (Sanskrit name that translates into "upward facing bow") is a rainbow shape made with your hands and feet planted on the ground for support. Is it wise to just throw ourselves into a complex backbend without warming up our bodies? It takes work to get to the point where your body is fully open and ready to experience the full posture; it can be harmful if you just jump into such a complex position.

Even in that first session, I loved the heat; I loved the intensity of the class; I loved the movement; and most of all I loved the repetition of the sequence. I was able to track my progress in each class because I was doing the same sequence with a few tweaks here and there. Even if my life was unpredictable, chaotic, and a whirlwind of emotions, I knew when I walked into that studio that I could have some peace because for that hour, I had someone else telling me what to do, and my body knew the sequence and the movement. It was like a moving meditation; I could flow freely through the sequence and get lost in the connection between my breath and my body for that one hour. I knew that when I was on my mat, I was safe to just be. When class was over, I would pick up the baggage of marital distress, financial instability, depression, and anxiety where I had left them at the front door. I loved the practice and the impact it had on my life, and that is where my journey began in 2015 when I finished my 200-hour yoga teacher training at a lovely studio in Fort Worth, Texas.

Why is routine and repetition important in yoga? Yoga is called practice; it is something that you do routinely to see the benefits for your body. With practice, you begin to feel the poses in a different way and connect to your body differently; and you can track your progress. "Journey Into Power" is the name of the sequence we follow in Baptiste yoga, and it consists of 53 poses and 11 different segments to encourage opening all over the body. The flow of each sequence remains the same, but we can modify a sequence and add in poses or take some away depending on the length of the class, the needs of the students, or the theme for a class. We can take things away from Journey into Power, but we must keep the skeleton the same to keep the body open in a consistent and safe manner.

What if we get bored with the repetition and consistency of the yoga sequence? What if we need more of a challenge with more advanced poses? What if we need a slow and gentle class geared toward breathwork and being still? The beauty of the set sequence is that we can still modify it for what we need that day, and the same is true for our prayer life and the Lord's Prayer. For both practices, we are able to shift and adjust the skeleton of what is important to address other things we need at that time. For instance, if Sally's hips are bothering her, we can go through our Journey into Power sequence and add more time to focus on the release and opening of the hips. If Sally is having a hard time forgiving someone for hurting her or betraying her, we may spend more time praying for forgiveness in her heart instead of thanking the Lord for dinner.

Persistence and patience are the two pieces that will enable us to continue the practice on our mats. Over time, persistence builds stamina and increases flexibility and strength. No yoga class is exactly like another just as no prayers are the same. There are different points of emphasis in both practices at different times. Teachers and instructors are all unique in their offerings, and one teacher will not be the same as another. Their tone, mannerisms, energy level, and personality will make a class different from the one before it even if it is the same set sequence.

We are creatures of habit and long for a routine that we know has a familiar feel. The underlying and most important piece remains the same while the outer pieces can shift and adjust to a more specific need in our body, mind, or prayer life.

Self-Inquiry

Do you find yourself in a prayer rut? Are the words just coming out with no connection or feeling? What is the main piece of the prayer?

What to Pray

Then you will call on me and come and pray to me, and I will listen to you. You will seek me and find me when you seek me with all your heart.

—Jeremiah 29:12–13

The LORD is near to all who call on him, to all who call on him in truth.

—Psalm 145:18

Digging Deeper

Write out the main points that you typically pray over. Then try doing something out of the box. Try to walk and talk with the Lord. While you walk, you can see new things that you typically may not have prayed for before. This is an opportunity to get moving while talking to the Lord and giving him praise for all the things that you see.

REFLECTION
SWAYING AND STEADY

In a recent class, I shared something that has been on my heart for a while, so I will share with you too. It goes hand in hand with sthira (strong, steady, and stable) and sukah (comfortable, relaxed, and calm).

- How often do we approach a situation with a rigid approach or tight stance? What would happen if we approached it and had the ability to sway with what is happening?
- There are times that we should approach things with a strong stance, but are we able to approach the situation with a more comfortable and relaxed approach?

I said to my class: "In my mind I see golden fields of wheat swaying in the breeze. It's not just one wheat stalk that is swaying; they are all swaying. Maybe we can all start to sway and see what happens when we approach each other out of love, peace and being comfortable with one another."

There I was talking about swaying and telling this story. I began to sway while I sat and a few of my students started to sway with me as well. Maybe swaying is contagious. Maybe there is a different way to love each other instead of being rigid and hard with one another.

CHAPTER SIX
FOCUS ON THE LORD AND FOCUS IN YOGA

The more you focus on yourself, the more distracted you will be from the proper path. The more you know Him and commune with Him, the more the spirit will make you like Him. The more you are like Him, the better you will understand His utter sufficiency for all of life's difficulties. And that is the only way to know real satisfaction.

—John MacArthur

My world goes a thousand miles an hour, it seems. Go here, do this. There are deadlines, events, sports, dinners, classes, and the list goes on and on. We have many days filled with work, kids, pets, spouses, and home life that can make us spin out of control. Sometimes, it is almost impossible for me to sit and focus on much besides how many plates I am spinning at the time. We all wear several hats as well: mom, wife, daughter, sister, best friend, bonus mom, aunt, business owner, women's ministry leader, volunteer, mentor, teacher; the list of jobs and hats (along with each individual responsibility) goes on in a never-ending spiral. When I find time to sit and focus on the Lord, it takes me a bit to settle my mind and my thoughts and focus solely on him. Does that scenario cause you to have a difficult time focusing on the Lord?

What about when you are in the eye of the storm? Can you maintain focus on the Lord? We live in a broken and hurting world that is full of sin and heart-crushing consequences. Would you have a difficult time focusing on the Lord when the medical diagnosis comes back with negative results, your spouse has lost their job, or the family member struggling with addiction has relapsed? These are all things that can shift our gaze from the Lord, and instead of focusing on Him and His promises, we begin to worry about the future. Would such a scenario cause you to have a difficult time focusing on the Lord?

To be focused on something, we must have it in the center of our interest or activity. We can focus on several things at once, but that also means that all those other things are not getting our full attention.

> So, let's keep focused on that goal, those of us who want everything God has for us. If any of you have something else in mind, something less than total commitment, God will clear your blurred vision— you'll see it yet! Now that we are on the right track, let's stay on it. Stick with me, friends. Keep track of those you see running this same course, headed for this same goal.
> —Philippians 3:15–17 MSG

God wants all of our heart, not just a little bit, but the whole thing. When we come to him distracted, we are not giving Him our all. Think about when you are talking to someone and they are clearly distracted, how does that make you feel? When we focus solely on Him, He will speak to us, comfort us and give us the direction and wisdom that we need to continue on His chosen pathway.

> *My son, stay focused; listen to the wisdom I have gained; give attention to what I have learned about life so you may be able to make sensible judgment and speak with knowledge.*
> —Proverbs 5:1–2 VOICE

How do we focus more on the Lord when we are busy with life and our roles or when we get gut-punched and shift from worship to worry? The more time you spend with someone, the more you know their voice and can pick it out of a crowd. Make time to connect with Him and sit with Him where your focus is on Him and not the things surrounding you at the moment.

> *My sheep listen to my voice; I know them, and they follow me.*
> —John 10:27

Simply put: You *make* time. How will you be able to focus on Him when you are bustling around all the time? Create time when you can sit in peace and quiet to connect with Him in prayer. Start off small; start with five minutes and then slowly begin to increase your time. Find a block of time in the morning or the evening when there are no responsibilities and no excuses. Block this time off in your schedule so that you remember to use it for prayer.

Once you have the time designated to be with the Lord, block out distractions. You may have to go outside and away from your home and familiar surroundings to get away from things that fight for your attention. We love to be around pets, kids, spouses, and coworkers, but these are also a source of distraction for us when we are trying to focus on the Lord. If you have a worn-out place on your couch and you get tired of sitting too long, go outside and take a walk or find a new space that isn't as comfortable as your worn-out couch cushion. Get uncomfortable so that you are not so relaxed and cozy that you fall asleep and wake up 15 hours later and not knowing what day it is.

In yoga, there is a practice of a soft gaze or *Drishti*, which is where we put our gaze while we are practicing yoga so that we can steady our minds and concentrate on our bodies. In a society where we are always on the go, we have to constantly be shifting our eyes to look around at our surroundings. When we are able to slow down and practice yoga while maintaining a focal point, our nervous system calms down. When I am teaching a class, I watch my students to see where their gaze is and whether it is a hard gaze (i.e., using their eyes like lasers to force the wall in front of them to burn down).

A student's gaze tells me several things about them in a matter of minutes. If my student is looking around the room and constantly looking at other students, it shows me that they are nervous and unsure (we have all been there), but they may be comparing their pose and alignment to the student next to them and that means they are not in their practice. Remember that comparison is the thief of joy! If their eyes are shifty and they cannot hold a gaze for too long before they move to the next spot, that tells me that they may be disconnected, and their brain is full of responsibilities and obligations that they are thinking about. Again, they're not present in the room, not present in their body, and not present in their practice. On the flip side, if a student is staring holes in the wall and the muscles in their face are tight and tense while clenching their jaw and squinting their eyes, we have an issue there as well. Drishti is not a part of the practice where we stress ourselves out and make our faces hurt. I want the student to relax their face. I normally see this type of focus when the student has had a hard day or is emotional because they put all their energy into their "powerful gaze." Such a gaze is truly not powerful; it is stressful, and yoga is not supposed to be stressful. Aimee Hughes (2020) explains:

> Drishti is a single-pointed gaze, a concentrated still point that we cultivate with our eyes in yoga. ... This concentrated focus creates a strong sense of being fully present in the moment, with the strength and attitude of a warrior. Wherever our attention goes, energy flows. You might say that your attention is one of the most important and essential characteristics you have as a human being, for you can create great things with a positive quality of attention.

We can focus our Drishti on points in the body as well as on areas outside the body. Typically, you would look in the direction of the stretch or pose with a gentle and subtle gaze, and you can move your gaze as you move through the sequence to different areas. It is common to use Drishti in your hands, arms, thumbs, and looking upward. Sometimes, we are still, and we can focus on areas of our body with our eyes closed such as the tip of the nose or the area between the eyebrows.

When you remove distractions—leave your baggage (anxiety, depression, worry, angst, anger, etc.) at the front door of the studio and become present in your body and mind, then you are able to focus. You cannot focus on the things that are hindering you at the same time that you are focusing on your breath, gaze, and body. It is so easy to get distracted in class:

"Look at her outfit!"

"What kind of mat is that? It's gorgeous!"

"I wonder how long she has done yoga. Her poses are perfect."

Comparison. Is. The. Thief. Of. Joy. When the focus is lost, we miss out on what yoga is doing for our physical and mental health.

Self-Inquiry

Where does your mind typically wander when you try to be still and focus on the Lord? Have you tried to move to a different area to pray and seek Him?

What to Pray

> *Because he has focused his love on me, I will deliver him. I will protect him because he knows my name. When he calls out to me, I will answer him. I will be with him in his distress. I will deliver him, and I will honor him.*
> —Psalm 91:14–15 ISV

> *Therefore, if you have been raised with the Messiah, keep focusing on the things that are above, where the Messiah is seated at the right hand of God.*
> —Colossians 3:1 TLV

> *No, dear brothers and sisters, I have not achieved it, but I focus on this one thing: Forgetting the past and looking forward to what lies ahead.*
> —Philippians 3:13–14 NLT

Digging Deeper

Make time to get personal and present with the Lord this week. Just give yourself 15 minutes to sit in the quiet and connect with Him. Remove the distractions and bring your focus to what you are presently doing.

TREES AND GROWTH

During the last round of our church's 21 Days of Prayer and Fasting, I was thanking the Lord for the friends He has placed in my life. And as I was thanking Him, I saw a grove of big, strong oak trees all nestled together. He compared the trees to my friends, and I distinctly heard the word *grow*. I asked Him to use us to help bring others to Him.

Later, I did some research on trees because I wondered whether they "talk" to each other. I found that there was a tree whisperer named Peter Wohlleben (2017) who said that trees that grow in the forest support each other through a deep-rooted network. Through this network, they signal each other when there is disease, drought, or insect infestation; they even send alerts when their behaviors change. They share water, nutrients, and sugar for the saplings to help them grow. They protect the "babies" under their leafy umbrellas from storms or drying out from the sun.

There is a well-known saying, "It takes a village to raise a child." Well, it is the same for trees and their babies. They get by with a little help from their friends. Typically, when one of these old "friend" trees die, the companion tree isn't too far behind.

> *They will be called oaks of righteousness, a planting of the LORD for the display of his splendor.*
>
> —Isaiah 61:3

They will be like a tree planted by the water, that sends out its roots by the stream. It does not fear when the heat comes; its leaves are always green. It has no worries in a year of drought and never fails to bear fruit.

—Jeremiah 17:8

That person is like a tree planted by streams of water, which yields its fruit in season and whose leaf does not wither—whatever they do prospers.

—Psalm 1:3

I will be like the dew to the people of Israel. They will blossom like flowers. They will be firmly rooted like the cedars of Lebanon. They will be like growing branches. They will be beautiful like olive trees. They will be fragrant like the cedars of Lebanon.

—Hosea 14:5–6 GW

Each one of us is unique in our own way. And just like the trees, God made us different from each other. We were created to serve different purposes according to the talents and gifts He has given us.

When we begin to find our purpose and the people to support our purpose, nothing can stop us. We were made to grow and spread His word and His love like the branches of a tree. Go out and find your grove of trees, support each other, grow into your calling, and serve a purpose for Him.

CHAPTER SEVEN
ANXIETY IN FAITH AND ANXIETY IN LIFE

An anxious heart weighs a man down, but a kind word cheers him up.

—Proverbs 12:25 TLV

What is anxiety? According to the American Psychiatric Association, anxiety can be described as a feeling of intense and persistent worry, and it can also cause physical symptoms to manifest. The physical symptoms can include nervousness, restlessness, tension (muscles), an elevated heart rate, sweating, breathing uncontrollably, shaking, or feeling worn out and tired. Fear and anxiety are similar but different (American Psychiatric Association, n.d.). Fear is what we experience when there is a source of danger; anxiety is when there is an absence of a significant source. With fear, there is a threat to the individual; with anxiety there is a perceived threat, something that may feel very real to the individual.

The numbers of individuals that struggle with anxiety and anxiety-linked disorders continue to go up each year. As I am writing the book, I found that anxiety and its linked disorders were affecting approximately 42.5 million adults (Goodman 2023). The following chart compiled by the US Census Bureau shows a breakdown of the percentage of adults reporting symptoms of anxiety or depression:

Share of Adults Reporting Symptoms of Anxiety and/or Depressive Disorder, February 2023

All Adults
All Adults — 32.3%

Age
18-24 — 49.9%
25-49 — 38.0%
50-64 — 29.3%
65+ — 20.1%

NOTE: Adults having symptoms of depressive or anxiety disorder were determined based on having a score of 3 or more on the Patient Health Questionnaire (PHQ-2) and/or Generalized Anxiety Disorder (GAD-2) scale.
SOURCE: KFF analysis of U.S. Census Bureau, Household Pulse Survey, 2023

Anxiety is a huge undertaking in the medical field today, and Jesus was no stranger to anxiety either. The night before he was to be betrayed by Judas, he went to a quiet secluded place to pray. Scripture says, "his sweat was like drops of blood" when he asked the Lord to remove this burden from his life.

> *He withdrew about a stone's throw beyond them, knelt down and prayed, "Father, if you are willing, take this cup from me; yet not my will, but yours be done." An angel from heaven appeared to him and strengthened him. And being in anguish, he prayed more earnestly, and his sweat was like drops of blood falling to the ground.*
> —Luke 22:41–45

We read that He was "in anguish." Jesus was scared because he knew what about to happen, and he went someplace where he could be alone and pray. Jesus gets us; he knows what it feels like to have anxiety and be full of worry and doubt. But he also shows us how our faith can help. Fear and faith cannot coexist inside you; there cannot be darkness where there is light.

> *Don't worry about anything; instead, pray about everything. Tell God what you need, and thank him for all he has done. Then you will experience God's peace, which exceeds anything we can understand. His peace will guard your hearts and minds as you live in Christ Jesus.*
> —Philippians 4:6–7 NLT

Worry steals today's joys by making us concerned for tomorrow. There are some practical ways that we can use our faith to help combat anxiety:

- Sometimes, anxiety stems from a past sin that we have committed and that can engulf us in shame and guilt. Check for sin in your life; confess it if it's there and seek forgiveness, so it will no longer be a thorn in your side.
- Lack of sleep and rest will also cause intense bouts of anxiety because of having a groggy outlook on the situation. Get more sleep.
- In the moment of anxiety, it can be hard to be realistic. ("If we lose our jobs, we will lose our house, become homeless, and never live in a house again.") The mind takes the worst situation and prepares it for us in a big beautiful (ugly) package that just keeps getting worse the more we unwrap it. Focus on the present, not tomorrow.
- I am an instrumental music fan, and when it comes to anxiety, I will put on some calming Christian instrumental music where I can sit and allow the music to wrap me up like a blanket. It doesn't have to be instrumental; you may find some upbeat Christian music and begin to sing and

worship and see how fast your mindset changes.

- Don't just sit at home in your cave of anxiety. Go out and find something that you enjoy doing to get those endorphins pumping.
- "You have that problem too? I thought I was the only one that struggled with that drug addiction, martial issue, mental health issue, etc." Go out and find some people and make them your circle, so you have someone to talk to.
- Get physical—get on the move. Of course, the exercise method that we cover in this book is yoga.

"Anxiety is a lot like a toddler. It never stops talking, tells you you're wrong about everything, and wakes you up at 3 a.m."

—Anonymous

Yoga and the Nervous System

Yoga helps by shifting the focus on breathing and working the muscles of the body to help the individual become more aware of the present moment. This will help the individual to move away from the anxiety or stressor and allow them to get control of their breathing and cause their heart rate to decrease. Yoga goes even deeper into our anatomy and our nervous system than just breathing and movement.

How does yoga come into play with our nervous system and anxiety? Our nervous system is divided into three separate systems:

- Central nervous system (CNS)
- Peripheral nervous system
- Autonomic nervous system (ANS)

The CNS is composed of the brain and spinal cord while the peripheral nervous system has all the other nerves that are outside of the spinal cord and brain. The ANS takes care of the functions that we do not have to consciously think about such as blinking our eyes, breathing, hormonal releases, and heart rate.

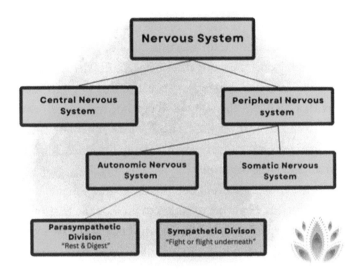

The ANS is composed of the sympathetic and parasympathetic nervous systems, which are responsible for our fight-or-flight and our rest and digestive functions.

The sympathetic nervous system is the system that is responsible for fight-or-flight. When this system is activated, it is preparing your body to go into action or into protection mode. When this system is activated, the heart rate increases to push more oxygen to the body; the pupils enlarge so that the eyes get more light and improved vision; and the energy that is being used in the digestive tract slows down so it can be used in other parts of the body (Cleveland Clinic, n.d., "Sympathetic Nervous System").

The parasympathetic nervous system is responsible for rest and digestion. This is the system that yoga tries to activate to relax the body and mind. When this system is activated, the pupils will constrict to limit the light, heart rate lowers, and the digestive tract increases activity to help with the digestion of food (Cleveland Clinic, n.d., "Parasympathetic Nervous System").

The Vagus nerve is a set of two nerves (left and right) that stem from the back of head and branches into several major internal organs. This nerve is a part of the parasympathetic nervous system; it is responsible for alerting the body if there is danger in order to kick off the sympathetic nervous system. In Latin the word *Vagus* means "wandering" because it is one of the largest nerves that wanders throughout several of the major organs. It travels from the back of the head down to innervate the lungs, heart, liver, spleen, stomach, pancreas, gallbladder, kidney, and the small and large intestine.

When a traumatic event occurs or the individual is in a state of addiction, the Vagus nerve ceases to provide the brain with the necessary information as to whether the body is safe or not. When it is "offline," the individual will lose their mind-body connection, and this is where yoga comes onto the main stage.

Yoga and the Physical Body

Yoga brings awareness to the mind and the body connection. Yoga's main job is to bring the individual back into their body and reconnect to themselves. The physical aspect of yoga involves moving the body and being aware of what is happening in different areas. Yoga encourages the practitioner to feel their muscles engage, to feel the floor beneath them, to check in with their breath, and to have a calm and steady focal point.

"How does it feel when you press your right heel into the ground in a crescent lunge?"

"Can you feel your foot planted firmly on the ground as you lift your right foot off the ground in a balance pose?"

"Are your teeth grinding together as you are in this pose?

Can you release them and relax your jaw to allow the tension to dissipate in this moment?"

These are physical cues we can use to try to get the individual back into their body so they are not thinking about either the future because they are not there yet or the events in the past because the brain will relive the traumatic event over and over to protect the body. Yoga encourages the practitioner to be fully in the moment and present; that is where the healing begins.

Yoga and Breathwork

Another aspect of yoga involves using breathwork to encourage the body to kick into the parasympathetic nervous system instead of the sympathetic nervous system. Several breathing exercises are easy to start and keep in mind when stress or anxiety shows up.

Alternate nostril breathing is a breathing practice that will help to open up both nostrils and can be stimulating for the brain. There are several ways to set up for this exercise, but it is important that the student is comfortable while doing this exercise. Typically, the thumb and pinky finger are the two fingers that are in control and alternate between the left and right nostril. However, if these are not comfortable to use, this practice can be worked with different fingers; it is up to the student on what they choose to do.

To do the alternate breathing exercise, the student takes their right pinky and places it on the left nostril to block that side of the nose. Next the student inhales through the right nostril and then switches over to block the right nostril with the right thumb. The exhale would come out of the left nostril; then the next inhale would come in through the left nostril, and the exhale would come out of the right nostril as the finger placement switches back and forth between the breaths. Alternate nostril breathing can relax the individual and create a still and calm mind.

ALTERNATE NOSTRIL BREATHING

Another popular breathing exercise is called box breathing; this one was used in the military for individuals with post-traumatic stress disorder as well as in tactical breathing. This and any other breathing exercise should only be used when it is appropriate. If the student struggles to hold their breath for the count of four, then reduce the amount of time the breath is held. Sometimes, breathing exercises can induce anxiety in participants, so the use of this practice will be different for each individual.

There are a few options for the student to try when box breathing. Some find it helpful to physically draw a box with their fingers on the space in front of them, while others prefer to do draw the box mentally. Thinking about the bottom left corner of a box, take a breath in to the count of four, hold the breath for four as you close the top of the box, exhale to the count of 4 to create the right side of the box and then hold at the bottom of the exhale to close the box.

BOX BREATHING TECHNIQUE

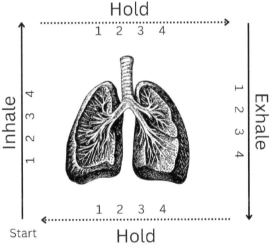

This gives the student a visual of a box where they need to focus on drawing a box either in their mind or physically. This technique will slow the breathing down and give them something else to focus on instead of the event causing anxiety or panic.

Self-Inquiry

What is one thing that invokes feelings of anxiety in you?

What to Pray

"Therefore I tell you, do not worry about your life, what you will eat or drink; or about your body, what you will wear. Is not life more than food, and the body more than clothes? Look at the birds of the air; they do not sow or reap or store away in barns, and yet your heavenly Father feeds them. Are you not much more valuable than they? Can any one of you by worrying add a single hour to your life?

"And why do you worry about clothes? See how the flowers of the field grow. They do not labor or spin. Yet I tell you that not even Solomon in all his splendor was dressed like one of these. If that is how God clothes the grass of the field, which is here today and tomorrow is thrown into the fire, will he not much more clothe you—you of little faith? So do not worry, saying, 'What shall we eat?' or 'What shall we drink?' or 'What shall we wear?' For the pagans run after all these things, and your heavenly Father knows that you need them. But seek first his kingdom and his righteousness, and all these things will be given to you as well. Therefore do not worry about tomorrow, for tomorrow will worry about itself. Each day has enough trouble of its own."

—Matthew 6:25–34

Digging Deeper

Take time this week to see what sparks your anxiety. How do you react? Write down your troubles and petition God to help you relieve these. Pray over your list every day and see how He moves in your life. He will comfort you; take time this week to open your heart to Him and let Him see what your fears and anxieties are.

ANXIETY, DEPRESSION, AND MY DAUGHTER

I feel like it's time to speak about my testimony about Jesus; it's been a long time coming. Of course, there is anxiety, doubt, and fear all wrapped up in creating a public post about something that I hold (let's say grip) so tightly—something that I have kept just between myself, Jesus, and a few people I love and trust.

I suffered from anxiety and depression before I got pregnant due to several things that happened in my teen years, and I was taking medication to help me cope. Then I got pregnant, and we had to find an alternative, so that I wasn't taking any medicine that could potentially harm the baby. So, we decided that it would best for me to stay off the anxiety medicine until I delivered.

My pregnancy was not bad at all—no morning sickness. I didn't even show until I was late in the pregnancy and had only a few months to go. I kept working and going about my everyday life. The labor and delivery were not traumatic; the whole process went pretty smoothly. All in all, the pregnancy and labor were the easiest part for me; the hard part came after she was born.

I didn't just have the "baby blues." I had crippling anxiety and irrational thoughts. It was late nights of crying and wondering why I felt the way I did—why I wasn't excited to be a new mom.

The worst part of my irrational thinking were the thoughts of hurting myself or even hurting my baby. There were nights that I pleaded with Jesus to just make it all stop, so I could be a happy new mom glowing with excitement and wonder.

This went on for months, and then one night, I cried out to Jesus to help. I needed help to get my mind right and to get myself out of the ditch. I couldn't pull myself out alone, and I was drowning. Why do I stand behind Jesus and my faith? Because He showed up that night and pulled me out of the trenches of the muck and depression. He stretched out His hand and told me to take it, and that night (I remember where I was, where Kendal was, and even what she was wearing), I did.

I share my testimony because I know in my heart and in my gut that this story will bring someone to Jesus—someone who is seeking Him. I know what it's like to go through postpartum depression alone and be afraid to reach out for help. And, if you are struggling with depression, I want you to know you are never alone. He is there for you, and you can always reach out to me if you need someone to talk to. You are not crazy; stop hiding your pain. ("Oh my gosh. You struggle with that too? I thought I was the only one.")

The enemy likes to make you believe that you are alone and mentally unstable to seclude you from people who can help. He is a liar; you are not alone. Talk to your doctor and be honest with them. They aren't there to judge you, but they can't help you if you are not truthful with them about what's really happening.

Today, I am so thankful for my spunky 14-year-old girl who is going to be a freshman this coming August. She is a blessing at the heart of my testimony.

CHAPTER EIGHT
THE DIFFERENCE BETWEEN PRAYER AND MEDITATION

For Christians, as for all people of faith, reflection, meditation and prayer help us to renew ourselves in God's love, as we strive daily to become better people.

—Queen Elizabeth II

W hat is meditation? What is prayer? What do they have in common, and what do they have to do with yoga and Christianity?

Meditation can be defined as a practice that involves breathing techniques, movement, or stillness to calm and clear the mind. Benefits of mediation would be to manage stress, calm anxiety, and create mindfulness. It is where the mind can focus on one point while concentrating breathing and our body, instead of focusing on what is happening around us. Can meditation be considered religious? Yes, and in some countries and religions, meditation is used differently, but for a Christian it is all about the posture of their heart. Prayer is speaking and listening to God to feel a connection and be in unity with Him. Prayer is a conversation between the Lord and the individual; it can be compared to picking up the phone and calling a dear friend.

There is a difference between Eastern meditation and Christian meditation. Eastern meditation is focused on emptying the mind and focusing on a mantra or something from within. Christian meditation is focused on the Word of God and storing it in a person's heart and mind to be used when necessary. We are to focus, meditate, and store God's words and promises in our heart and mind. Guided mediation can be used to focus on God's creation (beach, forest, park, etc.) along with incorporating Scripture.

> *Finally, brothers and sisters, whatever is true, whatever is noble, whatever is right, whatever is pure, whatever is lovely, whatever is admirable—if anything is excellent or praiseworthy—think about such things.*
>
> —Philippians 4:8

Meditation is mentioned in the Bible several times, and some speculate that Jesus participated in meditation when he was seeking solitude, peace, and wisdom.

> *This Book of the Law shall not depart from your mouth, but you shall meditate on it day and night, that you may observe to do according to all that is written in it. For then you will make your way prosperous, and then you will have good success.*
>
> —Joshua 1:8 NKJV

> *May these words of my mouth and this <u>meditation</u> of my heart be pleasing in your sight, LORD, my Rock and my Redeemer.*
>
> —Psalm 19:14

The problem with meditation arises when our heart posture is not in line with what God and his Word speak to us. We are to have no other gods and when an individual mediates, it solely depends on what the focus of the meditation is. Are they repeating mantras from another religion that worships and gives adoration to various gods, or are they repeating God's scripture and promises to store in their heart and mind?

Meditation can be used as a tool to feel closer to God and His purpose for you as you study and lean into what He says. However, it can be used as a tool that can be a driving force between us and God.

This responsibility is placed in the hands and hearts of the practitioner; these techniques can be used for the good of those who have a heart posture that is pointed toward God. Did Jesus mediate? Possibly. We know that he would seek solitude and peace while he spent time communication with God. Can Christians mediate? My answer would be yes; put your heart in the right standing and humble yourself before God. Speak to Him as a friend in prayer and mediate on His word to enrich your life and your well-being.

Self-Inquiry

Are you weary of mediation? Have you ever mediated in the Eastern philosophy or the Christian philosophy?

What to Pray

But whose delight is in the law of the LORD, and who meditates on his law day and night.
—Psalm 1:2

May my meditation be pleasing to him, as I rejoice in the LORD.
—Psalm 104:34

Digging Deeper

There are various resources available online for Christian meditation. Do a search online and partake in a Christian mediation or guided Christian meditation and then write your thoughts below.

_____

_____

_____

_____

_____

_____

_____

_____

_____

_____

_____

_____

_____

_____

_____

_____

GOD'S BLANKET OF COMFORT, SECURITY, AND PEACE

I have three blankets that are my favorites, and even though they are worn and tattered, I still hang on to them. Each of my blankets is from a different beloved family member, and all three have different meanings behind them.

The first blanket was given to me by my mom. It is an old, tattered blanket with cotton batting falling out of the thin fabric. She gave me this blanket when I moved away from her house in Georgia to pursue a new married life in Texas. This blanket signifies security.

The second blanket is one that I had a quilter make for my dad. It is made out of Crown Royal bottles bags, and it was something that he loved so much that he never even used it. It sat on the couch as a decoration. My mom gave it to me after he passed away unexpectedly. This blanket signifies comfort.

The third blanket is the one that my grandmother had in the hospital while she was slowly passing away. This quilt was created by women in her church, and they had used yarn hand-tie knots at various places in the quilt. It is called a prayer quilt, and each hand-tied knot represents a prayer that someone has said for the person who receives the quilt. This blanket signifies peace.

There are different blankets for different seasons or needs, but one common reason for a blanket is to make you feel like you are being embraced and hugged tight. Hugs indicate comfort, emotional support, and warmth when words may be insufficient. Hugs arise from joy or happiness when reuniting with someone or seeing someone who has been absent for a long time. In fact, there is a national holiday dedicated to hugging. It is National Hugging Day, and it is on January 21st.

What is the purpose of a blanket? When we were young blankets helped to keep us safe by swaddling us as babies. They are used to keep us warm and comfortable, which in turn, allows us to be at peace. Often, people use weighted blankets for grounding and security to relieve anxiety. Why? Because it feels like they are being hugged.

Security

> *The LORD is my light and my salvation—whom shall I fear? The LORD is the stronghold of my life—of whom shall I be afraid?*
>
> —Psalm 27:1

Comfort

> *Praise be to the God and Father of our Lord Jesus Christ, the Father of compassion and the God of all comfort, who comforts us in all our troubles, so that we can comfort those in any trouble with the comfort we ourselves receive from God.*
>
> —2 Corinthians 1:3–4

Peace

> *The LORD gives strength to his people; the LORD blesses his people with peace.*
>
> —Psalm 29:11

Do you feel like God's love is a giant hug that is all encompassing and provides you with security, comfort, and peace?

Close your eyes and take a moment to breathe in God's love for you. He is such a good, good Father to give us the tools that we can use to help connect with Him and take care of our bodies and our minds. He created all things, even yoga.

PÁV YOGA

Now that we have gone through the spiritual stretching, let's go through the physical stretching with some gentle yoga poses. These poses are designed to help loosen muscles, get you present in your body and bring your awareness to your breath and not focusing on the events, troubles or baggage that may be outside of your mat. Just bring yourself and take a deep breath.

NECK STRETCH
(ear to shoulder)

Come to a comfortable seated position and close your eyes. Take a few deep inhales and a few long exhales. When you are ready you can drop your right ear to your right shoulder and allow the neck to stretch. You have the option to roll your head around in circles going clockwise or counterclockwise if you choose.

After a few deep breaths we can move over to the left ear and take it over to the left shoulder. Again, you have the option to stay here and let it stretch, or you can roll your head in the opposite direction that you did on the right side.

SEATED POSE WITH RAISED ARMS

Take both arms up towards the ceiling and stretch through the spine. This is a good place to check in with the body and see how it feels up to this point. Continue to pull through the tips of the fingers as you lengthen out your arms.

SEATED WITH SIDE BEND

Grab the right wrist with the left hand and gently pull over to the side to feel a stretch in the side body and ribcage. You have the option to look down towards the ground or you can shift the gaze and look up towards the ceiling for a different stretch in the neck.

Transition to the other side for the side body stretch. Take the right hand and grab the left wrist as you gently bend to the right. Again, it is your choice to look down or shift the gaze up.

SEATED SPINAL TWIST

Place the right hand on the left knee and allow the left hand to come back behind you for support. Using the leverage between the right hand and left knee take a twist in the spine. There is the option to look over the shoulder to get more twist in the neck.

Take the left hand to the right knee and move the right hand back behind you at the base of the spine for support. Take a twist here with the option of looking over the shoulder.

RAGDOLL
(standing forward fold with arm bind)

Step the feet out wide and fold forward, grabbing opposite elbows and allowing the body to be heavy. Release the head and neck, and let the head hang down towards the ground. Option here to remain in the fold or sway from side to side.

WARRIOR 1

Start from standing at the top of the mat, and step the left foot back towards the back of the mat. Bend the right knee and allow the hips to drop down towards the ground. Reach both arms up towards the ceiling and lengthen out through your spine.

Mentally check in with the feet, and press them into the ground to create a sense of presence and stability in the pose.

Step back to the top of the mat and switch sides.

WARRIOR 2

Start at the top of the mat and step your left foot back towards the end of the mat (the back foot will be at a 45-degree angle). The right foot will be facing the top of the mat and have a generous bend in the right knee. The chest will open up in the same direction as the hips. Allow the arms to come up to shoulder height and relax the shoulders so they are not coming up towards the ears. Have a gentle gaze over the right middle finger.

Step back to the top of the mat and switch sides.

TRIANGLE POSE

Start at the top of the mat, and step your left foot back towards the end of the mat (the back foot will be at a 45-degree angle). The right foot will be facing the top of the mat, and the right knee will straighten. The chest will open up in the same direction as the hips. Allow the arms to open up with the right hand coming towards the ground and the left hand reaching towards the ceiling. The gaze can be down towards the ground or looking up at the left hand.

Step back to the top of the mat and switch sides.

CRESCENT LUNGE AND VARIATIONS

Start at the top of the mat, and step the right foot back to the back of the mat. Bend the left knee generously and keep the back leg straight with the heel of the right foot lifted. Allow the shoulders to relax away from the ears and reach the arms up towards the ceiling.

Step back to the top of the mat and switch sides or option to continue with the twisted variation.

Same stance and directives as crescent lunge only bringing the hands to heart center and then beginning to take a twist.

CRESCENT LUNGE WITH A TWIST

With hands at heart center, take the opposite elbow and place it on the outside of the left knee.

SEATED BUTTERFLY

Bring the soles of the feet together, and the knees will splay out to each side. There is also the option to fold forward will increase the stretch in the hips.

SEATED SINGLE LEG FORWARD FOLD

Extend one leg forward, and keep the opposite foot in towards the inner thigh. Reach arms up towards ceiling and then take a forward fold over the leg that is straight.

SEATED FORWARD FOLD

Both legs are straight and take the fold going as far forward as you wish.

RECLINED FIGURE FOUR POSE

Bring the right ankle across the left thigh, straighten out the left leg, and interlace the hands behind the left leg.

Switch over to the next side.

LEGS UP THE WALL

Slip a block underneath your lower back and take the legs up towards the ceiling. There is an option to scoot up to a wall and use the wall as leverage as the legs are placed up against it for more security.

WIND RELIEVING POSE

Bring the knee into the chest and allow the hands to interlace on the knee to help guide it closer for a deeper stretch.

RECLINED SPINAL TWIST

Bring the left knee across the body for a spinal twist on the ground. Option to have the left arm extended and shift your gaze to your left hand to encourage a twist in the neck.

Switch sides.

Once the stretching is done,
take a moment to be seated with the eyes closed.

Take the time to be thankful for the things that your body was able to accomplish during the time spent on the mat. Thank God for giving you an able body to move, and be grateful for the things that your body was able to do!

How often do you thank your body
for the things it can do for you?

How often do you thank God
for giving you the ability
to move and breathe?

REFERENCES

American Psychiatric Association. n.d. "Anxiety." December 11, 2023. https://www.apa.org/topics/anxiety#:~:text=Anxiety%20is%20 an%20emotion%20characterized,certain%20situations%20 out%20of%20worry.

Artful Tea. n.d. "How to Make Tea," https://artfultea.com/blogs/101/ how-to-prepare-tea.

Cleveland Clinic. n.d. "Sympathetic Nervous System." https:// my.clevelandclinic.org/health/body/23262-sympathetic-nervous-system-sns-fight-or-flight.

Cleveland Clinic. n.d. "Parasympathetic Nervous System." September 29, 2023. https://my.clevelandclinic.org/health/body/23266-parasympathetic-nervous-system-psns.

Duszynski-Goodman, Lizzie. "Mental Health Statistics and Facts in 2024." *Forbes*, September 29, 2023. https://www.forbes.com/ health/mind/mental-health-statistics/.

Hughes, Aimee. 2020. "Using Your Drishti to Improve Focus." *Yogapedia*. https://www.yogapedia.com/2/9597/asana/drishti/ using-your-drishti-to-improve-focus.

Kraftsow, Gary. "Yoga for Depression: An Integrated Practice."*Home*, May 31, 2013. https://yogainternational.com/article/view/yoga-for-depression-an-integrated-practice/.

Newlyn, Emma. n.d. "Understanding the Niyamas–Tapas." *EkhartYoga,* July 25, 2023. https://www.ekhartyoga.com/articles/philosophy/understanding-the-niyamas-tapas.

Shah, Sejal. 2019. "Saucha-Niyama: 5 Age Old Ways to Deep Detox Your Body and Mind Every Day." *The Art of Living.* https://www.artofliving.org/us-en/yoga/beginners/shaucha-niyamas-cleanliness-hygiene.

Shah, Sejal. 2020. "The Third Yama, Asteya in Daily Life: 5 Unusual Ways You're Stealing." *The Art Of Living* (United States), September 20, 2023. https://www.artofliving.org/us-en/yoga/beginners/asteya-yamas-not-stealing.

Winch, Guy. "The Important Difference Between Sadness and Depression." The Squeaky Wheel (blog). *Psychology Today,* October 2, 2015. https://www.psychologytoday.com/us/blog/the-squeaky-wheel/201510/the-important-difference-between-sadness-and-depression.

Wohlleben, Peter. 2017. *The Hidden Life of Trees.* Glasgow, Scotland: William Collins.

9 781632 966605